THINKING WITH FIGURES
IN BUSINESS

ROGER A. GOLDE

Golde Management Services

THINKING WITH FIGURES IN BUSINESS

Techniques for Improving Your Number Sense

ADDISON-WESLEY PUBLISHING COMPANY

READING, MASSACHUSETTS • PALO ALTO • LONDON • DON MILLS, ONTARIO

To my parents,
whose remarkable insights have
encompassed much more than figures

Preface

This is a book on how to improve your horse sense with numbers. The emphasis is *not* on what "good horse sense" is or on what makes good horse sense "good." It is *not* a book on interpretation *per se* but rather on how to go about interpreting, i.e. how to get numbers in a form convenient for interpretation, how to go about extracting the information to be interpreted.

This book deals with figures as they may pop up anywhere in a business—not only in the financial area. The accent is not primarily on increasing your knowledge of business or developing your ability to do esoteric computations. Rather, the attempt is to help you use your present business knowledge and computational ability to greater advantage.

More specifically, a crucial part of thinking with figures involves what, for want of a better word, may be called "pre-analysis"; a stage of getting ready to analyze, looking to see where to go. This informal phase of dealing with figures involves such activities as getting started somehow, choosing paths of exploration, deciding which figures merit attention and analysis, and seeing what techniques of formal analysis might be appropriate.

"Sizing things up," "playing with numbers," "scanning," or "eye-balling" are some of the vague phrases used to describe this fuzzy area of pre-analysis. Few people are able to go much beyond these catch words in describing what actually takes place in such pre-analysis.

The purpose of this book is to delve more rigorously into this area in an attempt to lay bare some of the techniques used by people who are good at "pushing the figures." Do not expect the solace of some simple all-inclusive way of handling all your number problems. This is not a book of the "Partial Differential Equations Made Easy" variety. Numbers in business primarily provide material for thought, and so this book must be about thinking—an always tricky subject. There is no way to make numbers easy, they just aren't. In short, *this is a book about how to think with figures, not how to avoid it!*

ACKNOWLEDGMENTS. I am extremely grateful to Mr. David W. Ewing, Associate Editor of the *Harvard Business Review*. It was he who first suggested that my ideas about thinking with figures could be suitable material for a book. Without his initial encouragement and interest, I might never have embarked on this volume.

I also wish to thank my mother, Marthe B. Golde, Professor Robert N. Anthony, Professor and Mrs. Pearson Hunt, Professor Gordon Kaufman, and Mrs. Peter Marks for their helpful comments and reactions to various sections of the manuscript.

Cambridge, Massachusetts R. A. G.
June 1966

Contents

CHAPTER 1

The Need for Number Sense

"It is not the talents we possess so
much as the use we make of them that
counts in the progress of the world."

Brailsford Robertson

Numbers — Center Stage

NUMBERS ARE INESCAPABLE

Numbers seem to be everywhere: in the news, leaping out of advertisements, applied to science, medicine, music, philosophy, and even sex. Housewives and professional men alike can rarely pass a day without dealing with figures in some way.

As a businessman, you are certainly handling a great quantity of numbers. Budgets, forecasts, or expense statements are not just "somebody else's worry." The employees in your firm generate numbers: ages, salaries, hours of work, turnover rates, and absenteeism percentages. The materials you use or produce also create numbers: costs, usage rates, quality ratings, scrap rates, or dollars of income. The increasing incidence of theft and embezzlement provides further cause for continued attention to figures.

There is more to business than numbers, but there can be no business without them. In the past, it was possible, at times, in functional areas such as marketing or personnel to avoid much dealing with figures. Now, numbers reach into every corner of a business and apparently will continue to increase both in quantity and importance.

THE INCREASING IMPORTANCE OF NUMBERS

From every point of view, business is growing more complex. Most existing companies are growing larger. More and more firms have operations spread over a considerable geographical territory, often doing business in more than one country. Add to this the tremendous rate of change in the industrial community due to new products, new production processes, changes in customers, new laws and regulations.

One dramatic result of this increasing complexity is that the businessman has become further and further removed from many of the actual events in his business. Often a manager cannot really know everybody in his department. A production man cannot keep his eye on everything and know what everybody is doing. Research people find it hard to keep in touch with sales and production people, and salesmen find themselves removed from the activities of the home office.

Yet the businessman has no less a need than formerly for knowledge of the business events which are occurring in his domain. As a result, he is forced to keep on top of things, using second- or third-hand knowledge transmitted to him via formal and informal reports. Using numbers in these reports is a convenient and economical way to communicate much important information.

A second reason for the increasing importance of numbers lies in the new techniques of management which are being developed. Many innovations in such areas as production control, market research, and investment analysis involve the use of advanced mathematics and of highly systematic approaches to management. This trend inevitably requires increased translation of business happenings into numerical terms. It looks as though the future will bring more rather than less of this.

Concurrent with the increasing complexity of business and the evolution of scientific management has been the development of the computer. This new monster demands that numbers be fed into it and spews forth what it has to say in numerical form. More important, the computer has decreased the cost of producing numbers. It is a well-known economic phenomenon that when you lower the cost of a commodity, you increase the demand for it. So the ever-decreasing cost of generating figures, along with the discovery of new ways of using them, is leading to an ever-increasing demand for numbers.

Horse sense about numbers has not become obsolete with the introduction of the computer and the emergence of

Horse sense about numbers has not become obsolete with the introduction of the computer.

sophisticated numerical techniques for management analysis. Rather, it is needed now more than ever. Those whose basic number sense is weak are exactly those for whom modern numerical approaches are just another source of confusion which they must either ignore or if at all possible side-step.

Number Sense

We have many senses that we use to explore the world around us. First, of course, there are the primary senses of seeing, hearing, touching, tasting, and smelling. In addition, everyone has developed various secondary senses. We talk about a person with a good sense of timing, someone who has artistic sensibility, or a man with good business sense. Thus, it may not be pushing the concept too far to talk about something called "number sense."

Business, it seems, is demanding from businessmen an increasingly high level of number sense. Yet for many people in business, the statement that "number was born in super-stition and reared in mystery,"[1] may be only a slight exagger-ation. Some businessmen just do not feel at home with figures. Others may feel that their number sense is not bad but could use some development.

CAN NUMBER SENSE BE TRAINED?

In the course of preparing this book, the author consulted a number of business professors and executives. Many reacted with interest but also with a fair degree of skepticism. Some claimed that "number sense is simply a trait with which one is born." Others suggested that "ability with figures is just something you have to pick up through experience"; or that "dealing with figures is really an art and therefore not open to a logical approach." These attitudes perhaps explain why so little attention has been paid to actually teaching number sense.

It is hard to disagree with the claim that some people have a greater innate ability with figures than others do. This does not mean, however, that one cannot raise the level of number sense one already has. Even the so-called basic senses can be developed. There are many moving stories attesting to the unusually heightened senses of hearing and touch devel-oped by people who have become blind. Perfume testers may develop their sense of smell to a remarkable degree.

Certainly, experience is an important factor in learning many disciplines. However much of our formal education is based on the premise that experience is more likely to have an effect when it falls upon a prepared mind. If you have the proper frame of reference, you can use your observations to far greater advantage. Aristotle once caustically observed that, "The way to play a harp is to play it—and that is also the way to learn to play it badly."

There is surely an element of art in thinking with figures: it is impossible to transform dealing with figures into an auto-

---

[1]Raised numbers are keyed to the "Notes" on pp. 201–202.

matic routine procedure. Nonetheless, insights into many "arts" have been obtained by setting up rational methods of approaching the subject matter. Yet history gives ample testimony that we tend to resist an orderly approach to a supposedly artistic or irrational area. The notion of quantification always seems to cause resentment. The entry of mathematics into the fields of music, sociology, and human relations has created similar controversy. Even phenomena like density, color, and sound were at one time considered unmeasurable and somehow mystical qualities. It seems ironic that a rational approach to dealing with numbers should meet the same kind of resistance that numerical (i.e. rational) approaches have met as they were introduced into so many other fields.

IMPROVING NUMBER SENSE

Developing a sense is not the easiest of tasks, for improving a sense involves more than just memorizing some facts. Learning where the keys of a piano are does not make you a pianist, nor does knowledge of the multiplication table make you a "numbers expert."

The Mock Turtle in *Alice in Wonderland* refers to the four branches of arithmetic as, "Ambition, Distraction, Uglification, and Derision." Even though you may share the emotional attitude of the Mock Turtle, this book takes it for granted that you have a knowledge of the basic operations of arithmetic. Hence, little attention will be given to the techniques of calculating percentages, ratios, averages, etc. The reader seeking adequate coverage of these topics should consult the books listed in the Bibliography at the end of this text. At various points, though, the fundamental character of some of these tools will be examined so that you may be able to use them more effectively. No advanced mathematical knowledge is required to understand this book.

Since numbers are the raw material with which number sense must deal, we will start the next chapter by briefly discussing the nature of numbers. The rest of the book deals primarily with ways of working with figures; that is, techniques for making the numbers more productive to look at, along with strategies for looking.

The approaches in this book are the result of observing people who are good with figures and of thinking about how these people operate. This is not quite so easy as it may seem since "numbers experts" usually work so fast that it is hard to follow their processes. Furthermore, they quite often operate in a more or less subconscious fashion and, when asked, cannot tell you exactly what they are doing.

Nevertheless, this book tries to make *explicit* some of the kinds of thinking employed by these so-called number experts. Many of the techniques suggested in this book rest on principles extracted from the interrelated areas of mathematics, semantics, cognitive psychology, and problem solving. Where possible, research results and knowledgeable opinion have been cited to back up the ideas presented. Little controlled research, however, is going on pertaining directly to the field attacked in these chapters.

COMMON SENSE AND NUMBER SENSE

Making the thought processes of number experts explicit can result in what appear to be rather obvious statements; statements which seem to be just "common sense." Of course, the whole field of business management is sometimes referred to as just "common sense." The great Einstein, viewed even all of science as "nothing more than refinement of everyday thinking."

But that *refinement* is all important. As some wag noted, "Common sense is what tells you the world is flat!" Furthermore, each discipline seems to develop its own kind of common sense. What is obvious to a doctor is not at all obvious to a businessman, and what is perfectly clear to a businessman may be incomprehensible to an engineer.

But obvious or not, there is the further question of what we mean by "knowing" something. When you know something subconsciously, you are able to use it only when the whim of your subconscious so decrees. If you can bring this knowledge up to the conscious level, it is possible to make much greater use of it. In short, there are degrees of knowing. There is a sort of mental threshold over which you must bring a concept in order to make full use of it.

Thus, some of the principles discussed in the following chapters may seem "obvious" or "already known." As a result, they will induce head-nodding agreement and little else. Nevertheless, be forewarned that the simple, obvious technique may be quite powerful and that becoming explicitly aware of the techniques will allow you to use them more effectively.

Knowing something consciously and explicitly can lead to better *use* of that something. However, this book cannot do much more than help you in the *knowing* phase. You, yourself, must do the *using*. The examples included in the text are there primarily for clarification—not for practice in using the concept. The true worth of this book can be realized only if you participate actively by applying the ideas being discussed to your own work. The French philosopher Montaigne preached that, "Though we may be learned by the help of another's knowledge, we can never be wise but by our own wisdom."

CHAPTER 2

The Nature of Numbers

A Brief History

To most of us it seems as though numbers have always existed. We take them for granted. It would be almost impossible to get through a single day without the use of numbers: glancing at the time, paying out money, driving to a given address (perhaps without looking at the speedometer), or looking up the recipe for your favorite drink. But there was a time when numbers had not been invented. Numbers are not something inevitable. They are not something created by nature.

At some point in the past (nobody seems sure exactly when) a primitive being asked: "How many?" The art of counting was thus born. In those early days, counting had nothing to do with numbers. The first people who counted probably used their fingers. Later they used sticks, or pebbles, or notches on a tree, or knots tied in a rope. The shepherd returning home at night could not be sure he had all of his sheep unless he matched them off one by one, against a pile of sticks. This procedure, needless to say, was rather cumbersome, particularly with large groups. Alice, when she steps Through the Looking Glass, faces a similar problem. The White Queen asks her, "What's one and one and one and one and one and one and one and one and one and one?" "I don't know," replies Alice. "I lost count."

Then some early Einstein began to develop the notion of a standard series for counting sheep: i.e. by starting with one sheep and adding one more sheep, and then adding one more sheep, and so forth he could count up to any size of flock he desired. The concept of number was beginning to emerge. At first the standard series applied only to the type of object being counted. Thus, some early tribes had different grammatical forms for "one sheep," "two sheep," "three sheep," and even "four sheep." Eventually this led to the abstract notion of number being independent of the particular type of thing being counted. Of course, numbers and words for numbers did not at first exist for quantities greater than three or four; sometimes for not more than two. Quantities above these small amounts were lumped into one category called "many" or "countless."

The notion of a number as a completely abstract concept continued to flourish, and various systems of notation were developed. It is curious to note that some of our modern-day digits are derived rather directly from these early systems of notation. The number 1 clearly comes from the straight line used in almost all systems of notation and originated probably as a representation of one finger stuck straight out. The figure 2 was represented by either $=$ or $||$. If the horizontal lines are written quickly, they become Z, and from there it is not too far to our figure 2. The same story holds for three, which was early represented by $\equiv$ or $|||$. This in some cases became $\exists$, which in time turned into our figure 3.

As better ways of counting and better notation developed, the processes of simple computation evolved: first addition and subtraction and much later multiplication. Mechanical aids such as the abacus were designed to assist in these operations.

As the art of counting was making further advances some troublemaker thought up another difficult question: "How much?" In other words, there were certain problems which just could not be handled by the simple counting of pebbles or notches: for example, the weight of a stone, the length of a road, the passage of time. Weight, length, and time do not represent discrete (separate) items that can be paired off with the standard series of numbers used for counting, that is 1, 2, 3, etc. So the art of measurement had to take a huge leap forward.

Consider counting as the comparison of one group (say sheep) with another standard group (numbers). The sheep were matched off by saying this sheep—one, next sheep—two, next sheep—three, etc. The next step was to develop standard units with which quantities could be compared, for example, a stone of standard weight, a specific unit of distance, or a given interval of time. Thus a stone of unknown weight could be weighed against the standard stone or several standard stones. Of course, any particular stone did not usually weigh an exact multiple of the standard stone. By the use of numerous small-sized standard stones, this problem was mitigated somewhat, but not eliminated. Any measurement of this kind was bound to remain something of an approximation. Even our modern technology has not yet been able to overcome this basic problem of inaccuracy in measurement. All that we have done is to develop smaller and smaller standard units which reduce the magnitude of approximation but do not entirely eliminate it.

Perhaps these early developments in measurement and the use of numbers seem remote, having taken place in an ancient world about which we know little. Yet, as late as the fifteenth century, elementary arithmetic was considered a difficult and advanced discipline. Not too many universities offered anything beyond addition and subtraction.

Moreover, the so-called primitive approaches still pop up quite frequently in our modern world. Those early counting sticks and pebbles are now manufactured and sold as educational aids to youngsters taking their first steps along the pathways of arithmetic. The early form of counting by pushing beads along a wire can be witnessed today in any pool parlor. Many companies record certain items on tally sheets by using marks to represent the items and a diagonal slash to complete a group of five: ╫╫ ╫╫ ╫╫ etc. The part of a modern electronic, digital computer which actually performs the calculations is basically not much more than a mechanized version of the old abacus.

Languages also show the numerical heritage of the past when "number" was less abstract and was considered a property of the item. English and many other tongues still make a distinction between the singular and plural forms of a noun. In Polish, there are four forms for the word *two,* depending on

So-called primitive approaches still pop up in our modern world.

whether one is referring to two men, two women, a man and a women, or two inanimate objects or animals. Japan and China still use the calligraphic notation of = and ≡ as their equivalents of our words *two* and *three*.

So the concept of number was constructed by man over many centuries. Starting with the early barter system and its later development into trade and commerce, business has played an important role in the development of numbers and computation. Egypt was a mathematical center of the ancient world and it is intriguing to note that Egyptian mythology claims that arithmetic was invented by the God of Commerce.

While business has nurtured the use of numbers, the reverse is also true. Numbers have given great power to business as well as many other fields. The extent of their influence is continually changing and growing.

The Character of Numbers

With the foregoing brief historical perspective in mind, it will now be meaningful to isolate several of the important characteristics of numbers. Part of the purpose of this discussion will be to pin down some of the intrinsic difficulties in figures. Explicitly describing significant traits of figures can be an important step in learning to handle them more effectively.

ARTIFICIALITY

Numbers are an invention of man. He uses them to describe certain ways of looking at things in the real world. John Dewey aptly states, "Number is not got from things—number is put into things."

ABSTRACTNESS

Much of the real power of numbers comes from their being abstractions of a high order. This may also be the reason why they require such a high level of concentration.

As abstractions, numbers can be applied to countless situations (or should we say *countable* situations). The same number, 5, is used in *5-Day deodorant pads,** channel 5 on your TV set, 5 product lines, or 5% profit on sales. In a sense, number is an abstract quality just as color or shape is an abstract quality. The color blue is attributed to any object which happens to reflect light in a particular way. Similarly the number 5 is applied to certain collections of items: namely, those collections that contain *one* and *one* and *one* and *one* and *one* items.

APPROXIMATE NATURE

Most numbers, whether they are future estimates or not, must be considered as more or less close approximations to reality.

---

* Trademark.

One reason for this is to be found in the process of measurement itself which, as we discussed earlier, must always give approximate results. Then, of course, errors inevitably crop up in the *use* of a particular measuring device, and mistakes occur in *reading* the measurement or *interpreting* the reading.

Furthermore, many phenomena in business cannot be directly measured. We may measure the efficiency of a workman by the number of units he produces, but this is only an indirect measure of his real efficiency, based on many assumptions about the quality of supervision, materials used, etc. Human abilities and human reactions are intangibles that are difficult to measure, but a businessman must deal with them and attempt to measure them. Product quality, consumer appeal, the effect of advertising all are areas crying for measurement; however, they lend themselves, if at all, only to indirect imprecise measurement.

To these problems, add the mechanical one of computation. For a trivial example involving the allocation of joint costs, let us suppose that you can calculate fairly accurately the cost of sawing a piece of wood in two. Now how do you allocate the correct proportion of the cost to each of the two pieces of wood? Does it matter if one piece is three times as long as the other or has a better grain and can be sold for more?

To top it all off, by the time a businessman sees a figure, the situation it was supposed to represent may have changed. The passage of time guarantees that past numbers will only be approximations of present conditions.

PASSIVITY

Numbers dumbly stare up at you from the page and make no effort to seduce you into paying attention. Of course, anything written or printed shares some of the same passivity, but words are more immediately grasped by the mind. Words can more directly arouse the emotions and provide emphasis where desired. When a novel is described as gripping, it is not too far from the truth to say that the words literally reach out from the page to seize your attention and mold your thought. One rarely has this experience when studying numbers.

REPRESENTATIONAL ASPECT

A number by itself has no real meaning. It is just an artificial abstraction. Ultimately numbers are meaningful because they refer to something. For the businessman, numbers are interesting because they measure or represent objects, activities, or events in his business domain. He reacts very differently to the figure 5000, depending upon whether it stands for profit dollars, number of employees, or square feet of office space. Because we act not on figures themselves but on what they mean, it is fair to say that they are not completely cold and unemotional.

Numbers are really a type of symbolic language. As with most such languages, there is need for continuous *translation*, from the numbers to the things they represent, then back into other numerical thoughts, and so forth. Numbers may represent something at a given moment of time past, present, or future, e.g. value of inventory. In other cases, a number may represent something's behavior over time, e.g. yearly expenses. We must constantly remember that the representations provided by numbers are only partial. Numbers (like other forms of description) can rarely capture the whole of a situation but can only portray certain elements.

CONDENSED NATURE

Not only are numbers a symbolic language, but they are a very compact, condensed one. Each figure stands for many words. Part of the condensation can be attributed to the manner in which we put numbers into groups and then group the groups etc.; i.e. ten 1's make 10; ten 10's make 100; etc. The introduction of the zero by the Hindus of Northern

India permitted them and us to indicate which *grouping* was meant by the *position* of a digit. Thus 3684 means 3 groupings of 1000 plus 6 groupings of 100 plus 8 groupings of 10 plus 4 groupings of 1. This approach represents a considerable economy over making three thousand six hundred and eighty-four marks on the ground. Even the Roman notation (which was quite an advance) required writing

MMMDCLCCCIV.

Overwhelming quantities of information can be numerically presented on less than a page. To write out in words the full meaning of a page of figures could fill a volume. There is just a great deal to look at in numbers that might be important. For example, on a report with ten columns and ten rows of figures (100 numbers in all) it is quite possible that any one number might have an interesting relation to any other number on the page. This would come to a total of 4950 possible relationships just between one number and another. Of course, this would by no means exhaust the various combinations of numbers which might turn out to have meaning. Sometimes such a situation can lead you to express your frustration in a rather compact, symbolic (and unprintable) language of your own.

What Numbers Do For You

In this introduction to numbers, we have looked a little at what numbers are; now we shall move along and examine what they can do.

INCREASE OF PRECISION

First of all, numbers help give precision to your observations. In fact, it is this precision, or specificity, which upsets some businessmen. They do not enjoy the feeling of being pinned down which comes with numbers. A businessman may find it easier to live with the general feeling that things are not going "too well" rather than with the knowledge of the precise dollar amount of his losses. A manager sweats a good deal over making up an accurate budget because it is specific and down in black and white and results can be compared *directly* with it. In short, numbers can sharpen the vague images evoked by terms such as "many," "few," "little," "a lot," etc.

AID TO MEMORY

Furthermore, numbers aid memory partly because of their *specificity,* and partly because of their *summary* character. After taking a plant tour and seeing various offices or work spaces, you will find the knowledge that the plant encompasses 150,000 square feet a convenient peg for your memory. Numbers help your memory partly because of their abstractness, which permits the mind to pull together related or associated information.

THE ABILITY TO COMPARE

Working with this associated information may involve comparisons in which numbers aid tremendously. Numbers act as a sort of common denominator, permitting the comparison of very different entities and the transfer of experience in one area to another. Thus, finding out that a plant has 150,000 square feet calls to mind the other plants you have seen of that size and their attributes, such as the number of employees, the amount of work produced, etc. Numbers permit you to compare time with output, purchases with sales, or one investment with another.

Thus, numbers are extremely helpful to you in sorting and putting together the thousands upon thousands of impressions with which you are continually bombarded; that is, they provide a systematic way to arrange and study the sights, sounds, tastes, feelings, and odors that make up the experience of your daily business life. Numbers can truly become almost another sense.

The Kinds of Information in Numbers

Let us look more specifically at the kinds of information that numbers can bring. An awareness of these types can be a very important factor in using numbers effectively: *The reason for looking at a given set of figures should influence the way in which you look at them.*

NEWS FROM NUMBERS

Just as you read the daily newspaper to find out current events of note, so you can read figures to learn about important corporate events. Changes will usually show up somewhere in figures. This *Number News* is a good way of keeping abreast of possible changes in your business.

INSIGHT FROM NUMBERS

Insights are a very special type of news. They consist of more than just facts. They penetrate beyond the facts, putting them together to develop relationships, uncover causes, and open new perspectives. If a cosmetics executive discovers that over 50% of his costs are going for packaging, he may suddenly realize that his company is in the packaging business as well as the cosmetics business. Or an executive might discover that his company is selling the same percentage of its products through chain stores as it did five years ago, while the percentage for the industry as a whole has tripled. These are examples of insight.

Insights may also be of a less concrete nature and may involve getting the "feel" for a situation. What is usually meant by this is *getting to know the normal or expected level and behavior of different factors in a company.* By looking at figures, a manager comes to "feel" that his inventory should turn over every two months or that manufacturing costs should run about 60% of the sales dollar. He is building frames of reference through numbers.

An important type of "feel" involves the interaction of factors or the sensitivity of different elements in the business to various happenings. For instance, a businessman may notice that when prices go up for his product, demand does not really drop off very much. Maybe he notices that because of a high fixed cost, a slight increase in sales produces a more than proportionate increase in revenue. Knowing how various elements of a business react is an important type of insight to be derived from figures.

QUESTIONS AND GAPS IN INFORMATION FROM FIGURES

Increased knowledge comes from asking questions as well as answering them. It can often be harder to find questions, than to find answers.

Numbers are a vital source of questions. For instance, if the figures show that your share of the market has dropped, the question immediately arises: Why? This may mean digging further in some other figures or requesting more information to help determine the cause of the decline. The specificity of numbers helps you focus clearly on areas in which information is needed or suggests vital new areas for questioning.

VERIFICATION FROM NUMBERS

The busy executive must continually make judgments or decisions and take actions. These activities usually require a great deal of intuition. Decisions and actions cannot always wait for careful methodical analysis, no more than a basketball player can take time to think out the best way of taking his shot as he dribbles around a man. It is just not possible to bring together and analyze all the necessary information in time to still make a meaningful decision.

At some point, however, it is important to check up on your intuition because nobody's intuition scores all the time. (The sociologists would call this a need for feedback.) It is important that you learn when and where your intuition or observation is likely to lead you astray. Like the basketball player, you need to check your scoring percentage from time to time. Intuition along with many other abilities, is capable of development and improvement.

For instance, there are many firms which continually underestimate the hours of labor required for a given job. As a result, they always underbid and tend to lose money. A look at actual costs compared to estimated costs would show management that the estimator's intuition was out of whack and in need of modification. For another example, it may seem to you that there has been an excessive amount of down time in production. The production figures compiled at the end of the week or month should help you verify your observation. If you decided to take some remedial action, then, at some point, the figures should again be checked to see whether your action had any effect.

Figures can be used for a slightly different type of verification, namely, checking on the merit of other figures. This is essentially part of what an auditor does. He assumes that many figures in a business are tied together in some way. Hence he checks and reconciles the relationship of one set of figures with other sets of figures. Executives should do this too in order to find out whether the figures they are looking at are reliable: Can they be trusted? How accurate are they? Do they contain clerical errors?

CLARIFICATION FROM NUMBERS

As a businessman, you may often be presented with a proposal: for example, a new investment, a change in compensation procedure, a new type of distribution, etc. Quite often such proposals are first thought about in general terms and are not supplemented by numbers. In order to see more clearly what is involved in any proposal, it is useful to present it with as many numbers as possible. It may be fruitful to work out a concrete example with numbers just to get a better understanding of what is involved. Furthermore, the numbers presented should not be numbers referring to cost and income only. If a new distribution program promises to increase the number of calls per day, the question is: *How many* calls per day? If an investment is supposed to extend over a period of time, the question is: *How long* a period of time? As Francis Galton once said, "Whenever you can, count."

The importance of using numbers to increase understanding can best be shown by the curious properties of the following proposal: changing the Gadget Company's procedure of giving annual raises to a system providing for semi-annual raises. It is assumed that this will help give employees a feeling of progressing more often, and perhaps more rapidly. This is all very well, but we need to pin it down a bit with numbers. Let us say that the same schedule of raises will be offered as before except that one-half the amount will be handed out every six months. Thus, instead of receiving a $1000 raise every year, Mr. Schmatz will be given a $500 raise every six months. Note how stating such a numerical example helps clarify the proposition by giving you a quantity to go with the concept.

To be sure, the scheme sounds fair enough on the face of it, but let us see how the system might work out if further quantified as shown in Exhibit 2-1.

You can easily see that under the new system, Mr. Schmatz's yearly salary will turn out to be much more than under the old system. In fact, the more years he works, the greater the disparity between the new and old systems. Even a raise of $250 given every six months will outstrip a raise of $1000 every year. This new system provides not only a sense of more rapid progression but also an actual acceleration of perhaps more than the company can afford.

Exhibit 2-1

MR. SCHMATZ'S SALARY UNDER THE OLD AND NEW SYSTEMS

	Old System	New System	
First year earnings	$5000	First 6 months	$2500
		Second 6 months	3000
			$5500
Second year earnings	$6000	First 6 months	$3500
		Second 6 months	4000
			$7500
Third year earnings	$7000	First 6 months	$4500
		Second 6 months	5000
			$9500

FIGURES IN ACTION

The preceding uses of numbers might all be classified as various forms of analysis or inference about the state of *past* or *future* affairs in a business. Figures are also used *daily* to generate action and to control the *present* workings of a business, for example, in scheduling production, budgeting capital expenditures, or designing compensation plans. Covering these uses of numbers is well beyond the scope of this book although such uses form an important part of management through figures.

We should not conclude without emphasizing the application of numbers to the future of a business. First of all, the past is primarily of interest because of what it can tell you about the future. However, figures can also be used to look directly at the future as happens in planning, budgeting, or forecasting, and although these activities require the use of projected or estimated numbers, you still get news, insights, questions, verifications, etc., just as when the numbers involved are historical.

CHAPTER 3

Thinking With Figures

"There is no expedient to which a man will not resort to avoid thinking."

Sir Joshua Reynolds

It is pretty difficult to turn off your mind. Thus, as you approach a set of figures, you are probably doing some kind of thinking. However, if you are really number-shy, your thinking may simply lead you to ignore the figures. Even if you gird your loins and decide to do battle with the figures, you may find yourself, when you confront them, powerless to do more than hope desperately that somehow they will surrender to you. This approach calls to mind an old limerick:

> There once was a breathy baboon
> Who always breathed down a bassoon
> For he said, "It appears
> That in billions of years
> I shall certainly hit on a tune."[1]

The issue is really how to improve the quality of your thinking as you approach figures, how to get away from a purely trial and error process. As a first step, it may be helpful to discuss briefly the manner in which the mind seems to function.

A Little Bit About The Brain

Theories about how the brain functions are far from fully developed and, as a result, are in a constant state of revision. We shall skip rather quickly over the existing knowledge about thinking, extracting only a few notions that seem useful for our purposes.

Many researchers tend to think of the brain as performing two functions: storage and processing. In other words, we have the capacity to somehow retain information and also the ability to manipulate or process that information. We may process it into storage, call it forth, and manipulate or transform it into new information. These capacities of the brain, marvelous as they are, do have limitations. Items stored in the memory obviously cannot be used unless they are somehow called forth into the processing unit. Since it is not always easy to find where the relevant information is filed in the storage unit, it may become necessary to somehow stimulate the memory by using something like a checklist.

The processing unit of the brain becomes easily overloaded. This overloading can result from both the *quantity* of data involved and the *rate of speed* with which the data are being thrust at the brain. Any sheet of figures throws a huge quantity of information simultaneously at your mind. Various research studies seem to suggest that *the processing unit of the brain cannot effectively deal with much more than seven separate items of information at one time.* "The ability to deal with knowledge is hugely exceeded by the potential knowledge contained in man's environment."[2] Thus, strategies are needed to protect the mind from overloads.

THE IMPORTANCE OF CLASSIFICATION

Many psychologists and semanticists have suggested that developing classifications is one way of helping the mind order the world around it. John Dewey called classification, "A repertory of weapons for attack upon the future and the unknown." In a classification, individual observations are lumped together by the mind so that it can escape bombardment by countless isolated elements. We are trained to classify from birth and it is, therefore, difficult, if not impossible, to recapture our early "unclassified" innocence.

Language itself imposes classifications on what we say and perceive, and it is difficult indeed to imagine the time when there was no language. Concepts and classifications such as *romantic love,* the *chair,* the *novel,* the idea of *success,* etc. have not always existed. It appears, for instance, that the concepts of "success" and "novel" originated only in the seventeenth century.[3]

The point is that what we see depends in part on what we know—including the classifications we have in the back of our minds.

TYPES OF CLASSIFICATION

In essence, then, a classification simply acts as a container possessing a solid (though perhaps ill-defined) shape. The way a classification is developed or expressed can vary greatly.

Often classifications are expressed in the form of questions. What is it that makes a *chair comfortable?* What is it that makes *production drop?* What numbers are *greater than average?* The italicized words all express types of classification into which you can fit information.

Sometimes a classification is expressed as a hypothesis. Chairs are probably comfortable because they have long arms. Production is probably dropping because of excessive turnover in the work force. Large variations from an average figure probably should be analyzed.

Sometimes a classification is merely descriptive: all chairs with long arms, all days of production under a given output, all figures differing from the average by a certain amount.

Questions, hypotheses, points of view, and descriptions all serve as receptacles for observations. They represent means of ordering the world you perceive and, in particular, of ordering the numbers with which you will have to deal.

For example, if you are looking for a reason why machine output is low, you may propose various hypotheses such as down time, absenteeism, raw material deficiency, etc. With these hypotheses in mind, you can look at the numbers and attempt to see which ones relate to your hypotheses (classifications). This approach certainly serves to reduce the confusion in the figures: you know what kind of numbers you are looking for and what ones can be bypassed.

THE IMPORTANCE OF STRUCTURE

Understanding has been described as the "fusion of a number of separate details into a single whole, in which the details form a pattern essentially present but not obtruding them-

Exhibit 3-1

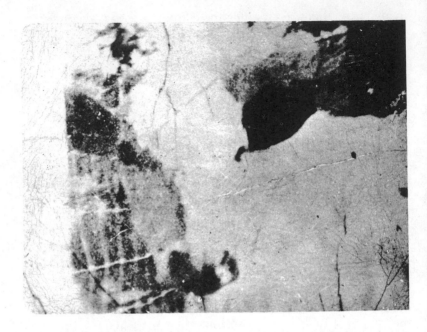

selves."[4] Structure is simply the fashion in which a whole is put together. Concern with structure involves finding the connections between individual elements.

Take a look at the photograph in Exhibit 3-1 and see whether you can make head or tail out of it. The photograph is right side up, represents something you have seen many times, and does not involve any magnification or other trickery.

Few people are able to decipher this strange photograph until they are given some idea of what to look for. Does it help to know that in this case it is literally a question of "head" rather than "tail"? In fact, the photo shows an animal head. If you cannot yet put the picture together, perhaps knowing that the animal is a cow will help. Have you got it yet? Maybe you should know that the cow's head is facing you full front with its ears sticking out on each side. If you still do not see it, take a look at Exhibit 3-2.

You were able to understand the picture only after you comprehended the *structure* of the various light and dark patches. Looking at figures can involve the same kind of problem; i.e. understanding depends on seeing structure. Structure and classification are of course related and complementary. Most of the following chapters are concerned in one way or another with the development of classifications or structures which help pave the way for extracting business insights from figures.

Think Before You Look

Alice in Wonderland asks the Cheshire Cat which way she ought to go. The Cat replies, "That depends a good deal on where you want to get to." Alice says, "I don't much care where—" To which the Cat replies, "Then it doesn't matter which way you go."

The way you go about looking at figures depends a great deal on where you are trying to get to. That is, the types of classifications and structures you should use will depend a great deal on what you are trying to do. To take a crude example, if you are interested in the efficiency of salesmen, the latest report on factory overhead will probably not help you much. Unfortunately things are not usually this obvious. In general, you have many possible goals or purposes for looking at a given set of figures.

If you are concerned with getting corporate "news," you will look at the figures in one way. If you are trying to *verify* the results of some action you have taken, you will choose a different approach. Think how differently you read a newspaper to get the general news from the way you read an article that bears directly on something of interest to you.

Exhibit 3-2

KNOWING IN ADVANCE WHAT TO LOOK FOR

In the mystery photograph of Exhibit 3-1, once you knew what you were looking for, it was easy to find it. Similarly, as you think before you look, try to pin down just what it is you are searching for. If, in studying a sales report by state, you want to know whether sales are greater in Georgia or Massachusetts, you will know exactly which figures to concentrate on. Even if you do not know exactly what you are trying to find, you will certainly have some hunches or hypotheses which will suggest which figures and relationships should be looked at in detail.

Raising questions is an excellent technique for digging into figures. The more specific the questions, the better. Remember that most problems can be stated as questions, and that an unasked question is usually not answered.

Vague questions inevitably lead to vague answers, since the terms of the question tend to determine the terms of the answer. Ask somebody what the sales situation in his business is. You will probably receive a retort such as, "Oh, things are going pretty well," which is not a very informative answer. However, your question was not very specific. Try asking something like, "In how many states did you sell over $10,000 last year?" If your friend is willing and able to answer, you may find out something meaningful.

Your questions and purposes for looking at figures can have many dimensions, a few of which are listed below:

a) Are you looking for news, verification, questions, or answers?
b) What news, verification, questions, or answers are of interest?
c) How certain do you need to be about what you find?
d) How much time do you have?

Considering these kinds of factors helps you pin down what to look for and at the same time gives you some idea of how to go about looking.

Thinking about what to look for can center on two types of concepts: particular business knowledge and numerical approaches. Naturally these two approaches are interrelated and not completely separable. Let us examine the first approach, using business knowledge to think about the figures. At any one time, you probably have a great many areas of potential business interest; so many, in fact, that you cannot keep them all uppermost in your mind, and that you cannot check through all of them each time you look at the numbers. In fact, you would be well advised not to search out too many things at the same time. You just create an overload situation which bogs down the functioning of your mind. It becomes extremely important to *think about the priorities involved* in your various interests, but even using priorities is hardly a complete solution to juggling all your business interests.

The situation is further complicated by the problem of change. There will always be important situations developing of which you will be totally unaware. Obviously you cannot decide to specifically hunt out something when you are not aware that it exists. Of course, sometimes the format of the figures (columnar headings, arrangement of the numbers, etc.) can be helpful, but usually the format does not change even though new situations are always being presented by the numbers. Furthermore, a report typically goes to several people each of whom will have individual concerns, and the report format simply cannot accommodate all of these diverse interests.

There is, however, another way of approaching the dialogue with numbers. You can develop numerical ways of thinking before you look that is, you can learn *numerical approaches for scanning the figures which, although somewhat independent of particular business situations, have a high probability of signaling important areas from a business point of view.* It is to this numerical way of thinking with figures that the major emphasis is given in following chapters.

Visualization Is Vital

Thinking *before* you look at the figures is the most important preparation you can make. *Thinking in pictures (visualization) about what the figures mean* is the most important thing you can do *while* looking at the numbers.

Thinking with figures differs a great deal from mere record keeping where the meaning of the numbers can sometimes safely be ignored. Clerks (or machines) can learn to automatically post the figures from the middle of one page into the right-hand column of another page. Accountants can give the impression that their sole concern is to make debits equal credits. For instance, an accountant was explaining to an executive some financial reports he had pulled together on a plant construction project. The executive kept pointing out the window to the building in progress and asking where this particular parcel of land was reflected in the figures or where that wing of the building was included, etc. The accountant kept saying that he had taken the figures off the books, that they were perfectly in balance, and thus everything had to be in order.

As a businessman, you are not merely concerned with record keeping but must also be concerned with what the figures represent. In the first chapter, it was pointed out that numbers are representations of objects, events, and activities in the corporate environment. Someone or some machine has translated those events and activities into numbers. You must translate them back before they can be fully understood and analyzed.

For most people, it is easier to think in terms of images than anything else, and this is why visualization of figures is so vital. The sales of a magazine such as *Life* certainly seem to bear out the old adage that, "One picture is worth a thousand words"—and perhaps 500 numbers. It is intriguing to note that some people actually have the capacity to visualize numbers in what have been called "number forms"; that is, they think of numbers as laid out along a straight line, or a circle, or a more complicated configuration, and when they deal with figures they see these "number forms" and manipulate them. Other so-called calculating prodigies claim to actually see the numbers in front of them as they mentally perform complicated calculations.

The kind of visualization we are talking about here is a little different. It is not a question of actually seeing numbers but of visualizing what they represent. Some things are easy to imagine: a room full of inventory, a batch of rejected products, the size of a new plant, etc. Others, however, are not so easy to visualize: a variance between budgeted and actual expense due to the volume of production, a projected return-on-investment percentage, or a liquidity ratio. Nonetheless, visualizations are almost always possible although each person's visualization may take an individual form. For example, the return-on-investment figure may cause you to visualize the particular machine to be purchased along with the labor to be saved, or perhaps a picture of the extra production to be realized from the machine, and so forth.

Sometimes the units in which numbers are expressed can provide help in visualization: the term "square feet" suggests various kinds of buildings, while the term "man-hours" suggests people working at some job. Another aid is to think about the following list which should apply to almost any number, past or projected:

a) What person or thing generates the action or observation?
b) What person or thing is acted upon or observed?
c) What kind of action or observation is involved?
d) What is the scene of the action or observation?

The point is that most of the numbers used in business are generated by some sort of visual reality. If the production rate of a machine drops, the figure portraying this decrease may take many forms: a percentage of last month's production, an absolute number, a deviation from normal production, etc. Now, any of these numbers should trigger the image of the machine producing less than expected. You may imagine the machine broken down and undergoing repair; you may see a bungling workman struggling with the machine; perhaps you may imagine some faulty raw material tying up the machine. Through visualization, you can generate insights and perceptions which will have important bearing on decisions and actions.

Sometimes you may try to visualize a particular number and find that you cannot do so. This can be important, since frequently this inability is due to an inadequate understanding of just what the number is supposed to represent. You should feel no embarrassment at occasionally having to find out what a particular number means. Numbers are a language—used differently by every company and often differently by various individuals within a company. Just as you occasionally look up a new word in a dictionary, so you will find it necessary from time to time to look up a new number and add its meaning to your business vocabulary.

It is important that the visualization process extend not only to the *event* represented by the number, but also to the *process* by which the number is generated. Ask yourself: What kind of measuring scheme is used? Is the output counted directly or indirectly? Is the output measured by a man writing down tick marks or by a machine recording something? What has been done to this original number to turn it into the number in front of you?

It becomes all too tempting to deal with numbers as though they had an independent existence, especially when dollar figures are concerned. This may be convenient for computational purposes, but at some point along the line, the numbers must be tied back into the real business world. Moreover, when it comes to developing insights, the mind can cope much better with concrete images than it can with abstract numbers.

To conclude this section, try solving the two amusing problems below. See how fast you can solve them. (Use pencil and paper if necessary.)

a) How many cubic feet of dirt are in a rectangular hole 4 ft by 2 ft by 5 ft?

b) A Farmer has 3⅞ haystacks in one corner of his field and 4⅔ haystacks in another corner. In piling the hay together in the center of the field, the farmer let one of the stacks get scattered by the wind. How many haystacks did he finally have?

Did you solve them quickly? Now go back and visualize the situation represented by the numbers in each problem. Did you realize that no matter how big a hole is, there is no dirt in it?

In your mind's eye did you see the farmer putting his haystacks together? Did you then realize that any sensible farmer would end up with just *one big haystack?*

Visualization is not the only way of translating numbers. A few people who are not visually minded will prefer to use descriptive sentences or some other approach, but for most people, thinking in pictures is the easiest and best technique. Just think of being blindfolded and going out to the production floor or with a salesman on his route. You would certainly miss a lot of what was going on.

Figures represent vicarious trips to the production floor, visits with a salesman, and countless other voyages. Make sure you do not deal with figures as though you were blindfolded!

CHAPTER 4

Simplification Has Power

"Our life is frittered away by detail . . .
let your affairs be as two or three not a
hundred or a thousand . . . simplify,
simplify."

Henry Thoreau

Simplification and Complexity

A great deal of effort in the modern world seems to be aimed at simplification. Scientists search for new concepts that are simpler than the old ones. Manufacturers work to simplify the task of housekeeping. Managers continually attempt to simplify procedures. Why all this attention to simplification?

All these efforts seem to spring from the unusual power simplification provides. When some concept (or product) has been truly simplified, it is more easily grasped, understood, used, and applied.

In the field of numbers, simplification panders to certain characteristics of the mind. The storage unit of the mind finds it easier to retain simple sets of numbers, and the processing unit of the brain functions more efficiently when the numbers are stripped of their complexity.

What is it that makes numbers complex? It may be helpful to identify five types of complexity:

a) *Complexity due to the reality which the number describes:* A number representing the rate at which the savings from a given investment should be discounted in order to equal the cost of the investment is more complex than a number representing gross sales.

b) *Complexity due to the digits which make up a particular number:* The number 5,379,421.7346 is more complicated than the number 10.

c) *Complexity due to the quantity of numbers requiring attention:* A report with 10 columns and 10 rows (100 numbers) tends to be more complex than a report with just one column and three rows (3 numbers).

d) *Complexity due to the quantity of connections between individual numbers:* A report where every number could be meaningfully compared with each of the other numbers listed would be more complex than a report requiring comparisons only between numbers in the same row or column.

e) *Complexity due to the number of different kinds of connections between the figures:* Two numbers which could be meaningfully multiplied, subtracted, and added would be more complex than two numbers which require only comparison by subtraction.

The first category of complexity is one which this book does not attempt to treat. In this chapter we will address ourselves to the second and third categories of complexity and attend to the last two types in later chapters.

The following section on approximation suggests some ways of simplifying individual numbers. The subsequent sections on summarization and sampling will discuss methods of reducing the total number of pieces of data with which the mind must cope.

The Art of Approximation

(Why be $99\frac{44}{100}\%$ sure?)

The dictionary explains that approximation includes the notion of nearness or *proximity*. Approximation with numbers involves choosing a number near to the one you want (or have) and letting it represent that number. In business, an approximation is called for whenever, for one reason or another, an exact figure cannot be obtained. For instance, predicting costs for budget purposes almost always involves approximation since the actual costs just can not be known until after they have been incurred (sometimes not even then). In fact, we will not concern ourselves too much with this kind of approximation, since it is literally inescapable. What is of greater interest to us is the type of situation where we choose to do away with an existing level of preciseness or exactness in order to have simpler figures with which to deal. If your profit margin on sales is 4.2%, why not use 5% when figuring the impact of a particular sale? If a new machine will cost exactly $3874, why not call it $4000 for purposes of discussion? If your plant encompasses 21,462 square feet, why not call it 21,000 square feet?

NUMBERS ARE TYPICALLY COMPLICATED

The numbers which come across your desk probably tend to be complicated. The major reason for this probably lies in the system of bookkeeping you are using in your business. In order to make proper checks and reconciliations, books are kept very precisely, sometimes even down to pennies. Legal requirements of course necessitate such precise record keeping and thus contribute to the ever-increasing complexity of the numbers. Imagine the government's reaction to a tax report from your company showing income to only the nearest $100,000.

Most of the monthly and annual reports crossing a businessman's desk are probably made up from parts of this detailed precise set of records. Even data collected for special managerial purposes tend to appear in this complicated, exact form, since it seems easier to simply transcribe figures without change. Nonetheless, this does not mean that precise data are in the form most suitable for your needs. In other words, figures to be used by management for analysis, planning, and decision making do not usually have to be as accurate as those intended for record keeping and legal purposes. As you can see, the numbers served up for your consumption may not always appear in the most palatable form.

WHY APPROXIMATION IS SO FREQUENTLY APPROPRIATE

In an earlier chapter, we emphasized the idea that numbers often represent physical events or situations which are difficult to measure accurately or appropriately. Many of management's decisions and analyses are concerned with the future rather than the past and, as a result, almost always include some very imprecise components. For example, when buying a new machine, management can do no more than make a rough guess concerning the number of useful years the machine will have before it becomes obsolete. Furthermore, many elements in a business decision are intangible, that is, difficult to pin down in quantitative terms. For instance, the adverse effect on union relationships might offset the beneficial effect of buying a more efficient machine.

Mathematicians tell us that *usually calculations can be no more precise than the least precise element used in them.* This is somewhat reminiscent of the old saying about a chain being no stronger than its weakest link. The point is that in business, the precision with which the elements of a decision are known can vary greatly. Often, at least one key element is known quite imprecisely.

The moral here is simply that all too often we have an illusion of accuracy because one element of a problem has been worked out to an exact number of dollars or to several decimal places. Frequently, this is wasted effort which could have been directed into more productive channels. There is an anecdote concerning a line of men and a line of women, in a room, approaching each other in a series of stages. At each stage, the distance between the lines is reduced by half. A professor watching the scene theorizes that the men will never reach the women, but concludes that in fact after a relatively short period of time, the two lines, "would be close enough for all practical purposes."[1]

THE USEFULNESS OF APPROXIMATION

Suppose someone showed you the two reports in Exhibit 4-1 and asked which report you would prefer to analyze. The odds are that you would pick *Report B.* It is also probable that the reports you currently analyze in your own firm look more like *Report A.* A careful look at the two reports in Exhibit 4-1 will show that exactly the same data are reported, but *Report B* presents the data in approximate figures rounded to the nearest $1000.

Why does *Report B* seem easier to handle? The answer lies primarily in the fact that it reduces the second type of complexity discussed, complexity due to the digits which make up

Exhibit 4-1

GADGET CORPORATION
OVERHEAD, SALARY AND WAGE REPORTS

Report A

Company Group	This Month	Last Month	Year to Date (6 months)
Executive	$11,158.03	$12,991.43	$75,989.41
Southern Sales Group	2,663.22	2,711.21	17,101.26
Mechanical Engineering	2,447.56	5,382.00	24,228.75
New Products Group	1,029.42	1,250.95	7,325.05
Corporate Planning	891.01	1,265.51	6,941.26
Basic Research	2,195.74	836.06	4,034.27
Doodad Division	3,071.46	3,341.37	24,043.22
Project Engineering	2,880.90	3,478.85	14,246.53
Operations Department	55,228.51	55,825.51	334,300.00
Marketing Department	19,017.80	19,239.12	120,076.00
Accounting Department	10,733.00	10,005.64	67,598.57
Widget Division	11,446.33	4,816.94	68,501.78
Gizmo Division	86.01	170.77	2,657.41
Graphic Services	4,549.22	4,045.09	28,487.09
TOTAL	$127,398.21	$125,360.45	$795,530.60

a particular number. Calculation with smaller numbers is much easier. To get the combined salary for the Widget and Doodad Divisions for the current month, it does not take too much effort to calculate 11 + 3 = 14. Similarly you can easily multiply this month's salaries of the Widget Division by 6 to see whether they are above or below the total for the six-month period. Thus 6 × 11 = 66, which is less than 69, the figure for the salaries over a six-month period. You can also see at a glance that the Marketing Department's salaries were about one-sixth of the total salaries for the month.

Thus using approximations greatly facilitates all the basic arithmetical operations. The chapter "Quick and Dirty Arithmetic" will show further applications of approximation.

Exhibit 4-1 (cont.)

Company Group	Report B		
	This Month	Last Month	Year to Date (6 months)
Executive	$11	$13	$76
Southern Sales Group	3	3	17
Mechanical Engineering	2	5	24
New Products Group	1	1	7
Corporate Planning	1	1	7
Basic Research	2	1	4
Doodad Division	3	3	24
Project Engineering	3	3	14
Operations Department	56	56	334
Marketing Department	19	19	120
Accounting Department	11	10	68
Widget Division	11	5	69
Gizmo Division	—	—	3
Graphic Services	5	4	28
TOTAL	$127	$124	$795

Much management analysis of figures involves comparisons: sales this year compared to those of last year or competitors' profits compared to yours. The next chapter will discuss in some detail how important comparisons are to thinking with figures. But making comparisons typically involves some sort of arithmetical calculation; hence approximation has great relevance to the ease with which you can make these comparisons.

There is evidently something about the way the mind works which makes it very difficult to remember and process complicated numbers. Who, for example, remembers the latest census figure for the United States in exact numbers or even exact thousands? *Few people can attach significance to more than two digits or three at most.* Very practical evidence of this

Exhibit 4-2

ACCURACY LOST IN ROUNDING 21,742

Digits Dropped	New Number	Approximate Loss in Accuracy
2	21,740	0.01%
42	21,700	0.19%
742	21,000	3.41%

can be found in the widespread custom of setting selling prices at, say $295 instead of $300. In this case, the merchant is counting on the customer attaching significance to only one digit, i.e. seizing on the "2" and ignoring the "95".

Feeding the mind only numbers containing no more than two or three significant digits greatly increases its ability to digest and assimilate the figures. The little you lose in accuracy will be more than made up in potential insights and analysis.

HOW TO MAKE APPROXIMATIONS

Remember that the problem here is how to make exact numbers approximate—something which is a lot easier than developing approximations where no exact numbers exist. The basic technique is called *rounding*. The word *round* implies smoothness; this in turn suggests what you do in a way when you round off a number: You get rid of all the prickly little digits from 1 to 9 that make a number like 21,742 rough and imperfect and turn it into a smooth easy (round) number like 21,000.

Technically, all you are doing is choosing to disregard all digits to the right of an arbitrary point and replacing them with zeros. This is the simplest kind of rounding possible. Thus, a number like 21,742 can be successively rounded off to 21,740, or 21,700, or 21,000. In the structure of our number system the farther to the left a digit appears the more weight it has. This fortunate turn of events means that striking out a few digits at the right costs very little in terms of the total accuracy of the number, as is illustrated in Exhibit 4-2.

Exhibit 4-3

RULES FOR ROUNDING

1. Start discarding digits from the right-hand side of the numbers.
2. Any digit discarded is replaced by a zero.
3. If the digit discarded is *less than* 5, no more need be done.
4. If the digit discarded is *greater than* 5, simply add a 1 to the digit immediately to the left: e.g. 21,700 is rounded to 22,000.
5. If the digit discarded is a 5, look at the digit immediately to the left. If this digit is even, do nothing; if it is odd, raise it by 1. This means that throwing away a 5 always results in an even number. The theory is that in this manner, half the time you will be rounding a 5 *up* and half the time *down;* thus 5500 would be rounded *up* to 6000, whereas 6500 would be rounded *down* to 6000. All of this seems to give mathematicians a sense of proportion and well-being.

There is a slightly better, more sophisticated way of rounding numbers than simply dropping off the digits not desired. Complete rules for this method are given in Exhibit 4-3.

IS APPROXIMATION ALWAYS APPROPRIATE?

The emphasis given here to approximation does not mean that it should be applied indiscriminately and always in the same way. Like so much else in business, approximation is more of an art than a science. However, it is possible to outline some of the conditions where approximation usually is appropriate and makes good sense.

One of the first things you should think about is whether the data are uniformly precise. As noted before, your results will never be much more precise than the least precise input. Thus, if many of the data being analyzed are vague or uncertain, it may well be worth working with rough figures throughout. For example, if two items in an inventory are being added and one of them has been hand-counted while the other had to be estimated to the nearest 1000, the numbers might look like this:

25,389 units   (hand-counted),
33,000 units   (estimated to the nearest 1000).

Now these two numbers can be added to get a total of 58,389 units, but it is silly to think that the answer has equal meaning in all five of its digits. The figure 33,000 simply stands for an unknown number that lies somewhere between 32,500 and 33,500. If all the pieces had been hand-counted, the total would have fallen somewhere between the following maximum and minimum values:

Maximum	Minimum
25,389	25,389
33,500	32,500
58,889	57,889

Why worry about the 389 when you cannot even be sure whether you are talking about *fifty-eight* thousand plus or *fifty-seven* thousand plus.

Many textbooks on business mathematics devote several pages to a discussion of rules for determining the significant number of digits in a calculation with numbers having different degrees of preciseness. For most business purposes, learning these rules just complicates life. *The overriding consideration regarding significance is what the mind can deal with.* Most of the data you look at will have more than two or three digits per number. However, since your mind cannot deal effectively with more than two or three digits, you simply need not worry very much about whether the data are significant to four places rather than seven, etc.

The necessity for approximation tends to increase with the presence of other complexities such as those described at the beginning of this chapter. Thus, the more data you have and the greater the number and type of interrelationships, the greater the need for approximation. If *Report A* in Exhibit 4-1 showed only two or three salary categories, the need for the approximations of *Report B* would have been much less vital.

There are times when you must look beyond just two or three significant digits. The proper time for this more careful look, however, is not really determined by any statistical rule of significance. The key is the accuracy required by the business purpose for which the data are being used or analyzed. For instance, close tolerance machining cannot depend heavily on approximations, and interest percentages on large sums of money may have meaning beyond two or three places. (Bond bids are often won on the basis of the third decimal place.) When the stakes are high or when a decision could easily go either way, there is a tendency to look beyond two or three digits in the data. But remember that no matter how high the stakes or how close the decision, the reliability of the data is not affected. If much of the analysis is based on estimates, you cannot improve accuracy by calculating other figures very precisely. When a decision is very close, nonquantitative factors usually become the crucial ones anyway.

We learn to approximate just as we learn any other habit. Every person has learned specific ways of handling numbers. When you are used to working with numbers to the nearest dollar, you may feel a bit uneasy looking at figures rounded to the nearest $1000. You may be afraid that you are missing something important. Furthermore, the Accounting Department will probably continue to serve up exact figures until somebody requests a change. There are very few corporations in this country whose management reports contain three-digit numbers.

In a sense, approximating is no different from using a scheduling board for production or drawing a graph to show some data such as increase in plant personnel. All these devices are intended to clarify figures and help the businessman see more clearly what he is looking at. Samuel Butler commented a long time ago that, "After having spent years in striving to be accurate, we must spend as many more in discovering when and how to be inaccurate."

The Significance of Summarization

"In conclusion let me repeat that . . ."

"So, to sum it up, I would say . . ."

"In other words, what I have been saying is that . . ."

How often have you heard a speaker use one of these phrases! How many written reports have you read that had a final paragraph starting with such a sentence! As a businessman, you are probably accustomed to seeing and using verbal summaries of some sort all the time.

Many businessmen insist that any written report include a summary no longer than one page. Perhaps you have used an outline format to take notes or prepare a presentation. (An outline is, in effect, a form of summary.) Yet how often have you thought about summarizing numbers?

Just what is a summary? A summary attempts to capture the essence of some material in a brief form. Its preparation typically involves stripping away the details and developing some sort of generalizations or abstractions. Examples or illustrations are usually left out. Thus, a summary is likely to be quite compact with a great deal of information packed into every word or sentence. In one sense, summarization is approximation carried to an extreme.

The significance of a summary lies in its simplicity. Omission of details and concentration on the key idea make information or concepts easier to handle. Also, summarization serves to highlight the truly important features of a report, i.e. the items that have implications for decisions and actions. By its brevity a summary facilitates retention and, curiously enough, a summary often has the power to evoke much of the original material on which it is based. By bringing to mind a summary, you may find yourself recalling a great deal more.

Of course, one can go too far. There is the story of an advertising executive with a poor memory who had great difficulty remembering what he intended to say in a presentation.

He found that clients did not appreciate his talking from notes. His confrères pointed out to him the merits of outlining and summarization. So he dutifully reduced his speech to an outline and the outline to a few key sentences. Still he found he was having great difficulty retaining the key sentences. He worked harder and finally condensed all the key sentences into one vital phrase. The phrase was a little long and still seemed to elude the memory of our ad man. So with incredible genius he boiled down the vital phrase into one crucial WORD that just overflowed with meaning and import and brought to his mind the whole presentation. Our friend wrote down the WORD, trusting that he could keep it well concealed in the palm of his hand. The only possible ending to such a story is of course that our hero went to the podium to start his presentation, discovered that he had misplaced the slip of paper with the WORD, went immediately into shock, and has never completely recovered.

Summarization can also be important in the world of numbers. The scale of summarization is a little different, though, from that appropriate for words. With numbers, even one page can be so loaded with information as to require summarization.

Numbers do get very complicated very quickly, one reason being that they themselves represent an order of summarization. Chapter 2 pointed out that numbers *represent* abstractions and *stand for* sentences describing various items, activities, and relationships. (Writing out all the facts and relationships presented in a numerical report such as Exhibit 4-1 would take many pages of words.)

TOTALS AND SUBTOTALS

Totals are a summary characterizing a whole set or group of numbers. In most cases, taking a total is not a very esoteric operation. It involves only simple addition or occasionally subtraction. One of the first things you should do when you receive some data or look at a report is to total any row or

Exhibit 4-4

GIDGET CO. (A SUBSIDIARY OF GADGET CORP.) DATA ON SALESMEN

Salesman	Sales (rounded to the nearest $1000)	Quotas (rounded to the nearest $1000)	Active Accounts	Assigned Accounts
Borsum	$246	$189	59	68
Droon	258	388	39	90
Gleeper	209	200	42	44
Murple	352	335	33	46
Plonth	260	261	45	52
Quallie	244	180	28	29
Snertz	212	193	25	37
Swonk	162	200	29	48
Zeakle	129	125	12	19
	$2072	$2071		

column where taking a total makes sense. You may be surprised to find that such totals are missing on much of the material you receive.

In general, dollar figures are totaled. Thus, it would be unusual to find a balance sheet or profit and loss statement without totals. A report such as Exhibit 4-4, however, is quite typical. Several important totals are lacking; such as the total of active accounts and the total of assigned accounts. One particular type of total which is frequently overlooked is the number of items in a set or group. For instance, in Exhibit 4-4, the total number of salesmen is not given, although this figure is an important total.

Subtotals are a very powerful tool of summarization. The way in which they are used varies greatly from situation to situation. You as the user of figures have to decide the kinds of numbers for which a subtotal has meaning and how fine you are going to slice your subtotals. (The ultimate subtotal, so to speak, is the individual number itself.) How many numbers you group

Exhibit 4-5

BACKLOG OF THE I.I.I.I. CO.
(INGENIOUS INVENTIONS FROM IMAGINATIVE IDEAS)

Customer	Type of Contract	Contract Price
Army	machining and assembly	$54,000
Navy	machining and assembly	22,000
Navy	study contract	5,000
Gadget Co.	development	11,000
Gidget Co.	development	13,000
Heigh Hoe Co.	machining and fabrication	27,000
Cosmic Astro Co.	machining and assembly	8,000
Cosmic Astro Co.	study contract	4,000
Mad Machines Inc.	machining and fabrication	16,000
TOTAL		$160,000

into a subtotal is determined by the degree of summarization that is appropriate to your needs. If you use too many subtotals, you may clutter your mind and lose much of the power of the summary; if you use too few, you may miss important information and lose possible insights.

Consider Exhibit 4-5 which shows the backlog of a company claiming to be in the research and development business. There are many relevant subtotals to be examined here. For instance, you may want to know backlog subtotals by customer or type of customer. You may also be interested in backlog broken down by type of work involved (study vs. machining vs. development, etc.) Looking at this breakdown, you would find that only 15% of the backlog was in research and development. You might suddenly realize that the I.I.I.I. Co. was really just an intellectual machine shop and not a research and development outfit at all.

Totals become important not only in themselves but also in the calculation of other summary measures, the most important of which is the *arithmetic mean*.

Averages.

AVERAGES

A *total* represents an abbreviated description of a *whole group* of numbers considered together. An *average* is a kind of summary which helps describe *individual members* of the number group. There are several kinds of averages, but we will concentrate on the everyday average known technically as the *arithmetic mean*. The mean is calculated by taking the total sum of a group of figures and dividing it by the number of figures which were added to get the total. Thus, sales of the average salesman in Exhibit 4-4 would be calculated as follows: $2072 \div 9 =$ about $230 per salesman.

Like taking a total, calculating the mean is not a very esoteric mathematical technique. (This does not imply that the average is not a powerful summary.) Averages, however, are not always completely obvious results. Sometimes the unusual aspect of an average lies in the items which enter into it. For example average sales per salesman is a commonplace type of average, but average sales per square foot of building space or average sales per employee are less orthodox although still meaningful.

At other times, the arithmetic involved in an average may be a little tricky and require weighting the numbers properly or being sure to use correct units, etc. The following problem presents an intriguing example of how elusive averages can sometimes be.

Suppose that you have a machine which performs a given operation in the manufacture of widgets. It is scheduled to produce at the rate of 300 pieces per hour although it can operate at higher speeds. One day you are processing a batch of 900 widgets on this machine. Some difficulties develop and you discover after 450 pieces have been run that the machine has been operating at the rate of only 150 pieces per hour. Part of the delay, of course, was caused by down time and the time needed for repairs. Assume that the machine is again in perfect working condition. At what rate will you have to run the next 450 widgets so that the complete batch of 900 widgets will have been produced at the scheduled rate of 300 per hour?

Your first impulse might be to figure that if the first half of the batch were done at the rate of 150 per hour, the second half should be done at the rate of 450 per hour since $150 + 450 = 600$ and $600 \div 2 = 300$. Unfortunately, this is not a correct calculation of averages. In fact, the surprising result of this curious problem is that there is *no* possible rate at which the second 450 pieces can be processed which will yield an average of 300 per hour for the whole batch.

You can see this immediately if you consider the *times* involved for the various runs. The first run of 450 pieces at the rate of 150 pieces per hour took three hours. Running 900 pieces at the rate of 300 per hour would require three hours. But you have already taken the allotted three hours to run the first 450 pieces. You would therefore, have to process the next 450 pieces instantaneously in order to finish all 900 pieces in three hours. Even with the advances of modern technology, such a procedure is not yet feasible.

In other situations, managers may work with an erroneous figure as an average simply because they have not calculated it out with paper and pencil. The mind has a strange way of grabbing on to some numbers in a group and ignoring others. Few people can look at a column of figures and come up with even an approximate estimate of the average.

Furthermore, the mean is often confused with other "average" measures. For example, the *mode* is the number in a group which occurs most frequently. Thus, if a group contained the numbers 2, 2, 3, 9, and 14, the mode would be 2. Since the mode is the number you bump into most often, it frequently becomes the value your mind retains. Thus, when people are asked for an average, they tend to give the mode without realizing it.

The *median* of a group of numbers splits the group into two equal halves. Thus the median for the group of figures listed in the preceding paragraph is 3. Half the figures are above 3 and half are below. Measures like the median could of course show you where other splits of the group occur: for example, one-fourth of the numbers are above a given figure, or 10% of the numbers are above a given figure, etc. So, statisticians talk about quartiles, deciles, or percentiles.

These two average measures, mode and median should be clear in your mind primarily so that you will not confuse them with the mean, the truly *typical* value. There will, of course, be occasions when you may be interested in the median or mode for some special reason, but the *typicalness* of the mean and its relation to the total make it a much more important and powerful summary measure.

Mathematics and statistics are full of other types of summary measures. Many are hard to calculate and difficult to use, and these will not be discussed here. It is, however, worth mentioning one other summary measure which is related to the *dispersion* of a set of figures around its average: for example, the dispersion of 3, 4, 5 is different from that of 1, 4, 7 even though both sets of figures have the same mean. You may get a worth-while kind of summary by loosely categorizing the *range of variation* in a set of figures even if you do not make an exact calculation.

SUMMARIES AND THEIR LIMITATIONS

Numerical summaries have some specific uses which verbal summaries do not have. In particular, you can use totals and averages to help you in the following interrelated areas:

a) detection (of change),
b) control,
c) comparison,
d) prediction.

When one element of a group of numbers changes, it affects both the total and the average. Small changes often will not make *significant* differences in the total or average, but sizable changes will. Thus looking at the total and average of a group of numbers will quickly reveal the presence of any significant change; it is a good way to see whether actions you may have taken had any significant effect.

It is this property of the average and total which makes them so helpful in control procedures. Changes in these measures serve as *red flags*. They represent the kind of flag waving used in *management by exception*—concentration only on unusual or abnormal occurances. The presence of a red-flag change in the total or average cannot, of course, explain fully the cause for the change but merely signals the proper place to probe into the details in order to find out what is going on.

As Chapter 5 will point out, much of analysis involves the use of comparison. Summary measures provide an important means of *comparing different groups of figures*. It is more or less clear how to compare the number 3 with the number 37. But how would you compare the two groups of numbers shown in Fig. 4-1, without using some kind of summary measures?

Prediction and forecasting are frequently done in terms of groups of numbers rather than individual entities. There are two reasons for this approach: (1) Knowledge of the future is so unclear that going into too much detail is not really significant, that is, you must approximate. (2) Statisticians claim that one can predict the behavior of a group (total or aver-

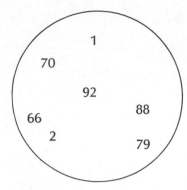
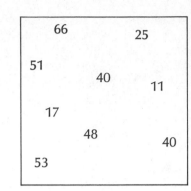

Figure 4-1

age) more accurately than that of an individual member because in a group variations tend to cancel out. As pointed out before, the weighted average really represents the best guess as to the value of a number in a group. Thus, if you were going to add one salesman to your force, lacking other information, you could estimate that the new man would sell as much as the average member of the group.

Summaries, whether verbal or numerical, do not, and are not supposed to, give the complete picture. Their usefulness comes from just this fact. But the incompleteness must always be kept in mind. You cannot reconstruct the individual numbers in Exhibit 4-4 simply by knowing their total and average. The columns "Sales" and "Quotas" in Exhibit 4-4 have the same total and average, yet the figures in each are quite different; i.e. some salesmen greatly exceeded their quota and some did not make it. Changes can occur which will not show up in the average or total and yet be significant.

Lastly, you should not forget that an average is just a mathematical figure which does not actually represent any individual member of the group, although it is the typical representation of a member of the group. If the employees in your firm have an average of $2\frac{1}{4}$ children each, you certainly would be surprised to see ¼ of a child toddling behind his father at the annual company picnic.

Summarization simplifies the battle for you by reducing the number of pieces of data with which you have to grapple. Any group of figures, however, can be summarized in many different ways. You should of course look with interest at the partial summaries already in the data as it is presented to you, but you will probably want to make further summarizations of your own. As you start to do this, you will find it but a short jump to *sampling,* which is the next topic.

The Skill of Unsophisticated Sampling

Spend thirty seconds looking at the Plex Report in Exhibit 4-6 and another thirty seconds looking only at the Pling Report. From which report did you learn more about the Gadget Corporation? Most people would say they learned more from the Pling Report.

As you may have realized, the data found in the Pling Report also occur in the Plex Report; however, fewer data are presented. (In fact, the Pling Report contains exactly 15% of the figures in the Plex Report.) The particular figures of the Pling Report were chosen more or less at random or, to put it another way, the Pling Report represents a sam-*pling* of a more com-*plex* report.

The notion of sampling should not be new to you since you use it every day of your life in some form or another. You taste only part of the soup to see whether it is cool enough, and you give only a sample of your blood to the doctor. The fact that television show ratings are based on sampling has from time to time caused some notoriety for the concept.

Sampling has been introduced into many phases of business life: Quality control testing relies heavily on the use of samples.

Exhibit 4-6

GADGET COMPANY NONSENSE PRODUCT REPORTS

| | Plex Report | | | | | | | |
Product	Total Cost	Profit	Net Price	Dealer Discount	List Price	Margin Percent	Annual Unit Volume	% Increase Over Last Year
Widget	$195	$26	$221	$69	$290	12	3828	8
Gizmo	14	10	24	8	32	42	2860	(10)
Gadget	21	13	34	11	45	38	3265	5
Whatsis	22	13	35	12	46	37	1420	22
Thingamabob	57	18	75	24	99	24	3436	3
Knick Knack	28	21	49	16	65	43	2796	2
Whatchamacallit	5	3	8	2	10	37	2659	15
Contraption	35	19	54	17	71	35	851	(2)
Murple	43	49	92	29	121	53	490	—
Quiddal	30	22	52	16	68	42	114	10

Pling Report

Product	Total Cost	Profit	Net Price	Dealer Discount	List Price	Margin Percent	Annual Unit Volume	% Increase Over Last Year
Widget								
Gizmo	$14		$24				2860	(10)
Gadget								
Whatsis								
Thingamabob	57		75				3436	3
Knick Knack								
Whatchamacallit								
Contraption								
Murple								
Quiddal	30		52				114	10

Auditors have started to use sampling in the verification of records. You do not supervise subordinates by checking *every single* thing they do. However, you may not have realized how sampling could apply to your thinking with figures.

Sampling, like summarization, is a way of reducing the number of pieces of data with which you have to grapple. A great deal of sophisticated mathematical work has been done in the field of sampling. Nevertheless, we shall choose the more informal approach exemplified by, say soup tasting, rather than the rigorous one of say, quality control. We shall, however, draw on some of the more advanced technology of sampling in order to suggest important although somewhat less sophisticated ways of sampling numbers.

THE PURPOSE OF SAMPLING

In the previously cited examples (both formal and informal), the main goal of sampling was to obtain information about an entire group or entity by looking at only a portion of it. In the case of soup, you are concerned with the warmth of the *whole* bowl, and in quality control, you are concerned with the quality of *all* items produced. This approach can be carried over perfectly well to looking at figures. If you are concerned with travel expenses, you may decide not to look at every travel voucher. If you are reviewing the number of calls made by salesmen, you may not look at every salesman's record or what he reported for every day.

There can also be a slightly different purpose in sampling the numbers that cross your desk. Most groups of numbers that you look at turn out to represent a collection of many different bits of data all related in some way to the same activity or department. Sampling a report, in this way, may be a little like reading a newspaper. You probably do not read every article in a daily newspaper or even every word of those articles you do read. You are sampling the newspaper in order to see what types of news are in it, not to make inferences about some larger entity from which the sample was drawn. Similarly, you may often sample figures in order to get an idea of the various kinds of information conveyed by a report.

Regardless of the reason, sampling of some sort is pretty much inevitable, because you just cannot analyze every figure and every relationship on even a simple report. The point is that you probably have not given much conscious thought to your sampling procedures, and so it will be helpful to examine the various types which you may wish to use.

TYPES OF SAMPLING

Random Sampling. Random sampling is one of the most commonly talked about approaches. The general concept of randomness is not a difficult one to grasp. In essence, it means lack of pattern or predictability. In a random sample, the chance of any one item being included is as good as that of any other item, and you cannot predict what items will be included by knowing which items already are in the sample.

While the concept is simple, doing something in a truly random manner is harder than you might think. You may feel that if you ask someone to call the flip of a coin he will call it at random; research, however, seems to indicate that about three out of four people are more likely to call *heads* than *tails*. If people are asked to give a random series of single digit numbers, they typically tend to favor some numbers over others. Our minds are not trained to be random instruments. From early childhood, we are trained to order everything into patterns, whereas being random involves the *lack* of pattern.

It is equally difficult to find a mechanism which can produce random results. The traditional process of flipping a coin is in reality rarely random. The coin is usually thrown in a biased way, and it is almost impossible to find a perfect coin (worn equally on both sides).

Sampling items in a rigorously random fashion is important because randomness allows handling of the sample in mathematically convenient ways. Fortunately for your purposes you do not need to worry about sampling in true random fashion.

Exhibit 4-7

A RANDOM SAMPLE AND A SYSTEMATIC SAMPLE OF THE NONSENSE PRODUCT REPORT

Pure Random Sample

Product	Total Cost	Profit	Net Price	Dealer Discount	List Price	Margin Percent	Annual Unit Volume	% Increase Over Last Year
Widget		$26						
Gizmo	$14							(10)
Gadget				$11				
Whatsis								
Thingamabob								
Knick Knack	5							
Whatchamacallit		19						
Contraption			$54					
Murple			92					
Quiddal			16					10

Systematic Sample
(every tenth figure counting across the rows)

Product	Total Cost	Net Price	Profit	Dealer Discount	List Price	Margin Percent	Annual Unit Volume	% Increase Over Last Year
Widget								
Gizmo		$10						
Gadget				$11				
Whatsis						37		
Thingamabob								3
Knick Knack								
Whatchamacallit		3						
Contraption				17				
Murple						53		
Quiddal								10

However, it can be extremely important to approximate a *random* approach. You must make a conscious effort since *the intuitive tendency is to select the same type of figure over and over.*

Systematic Sampling. One easy way of sampling in an approximately random fashion is called systematic sampling. This means that you set up a *system* which tends to produce a more or less random result. For instance, if you decide that you have the time or the capacity to absorb only one-fourth of the data presented to you, then you simply look only at every fourth figure as your eye moves over the rows or columns. Of course, you should start your counting in a different place each time you see a new issue of the report; otherwise, you will find yourself always looking at the same parts of the data.

If you wanted a smaller sample, you might look only at every fifth or every tenth figure. Very often when you see someone scanning a report he is in fact taking a systematic sample (perhaps not as precisely as indicated here). Although such a numbers expert may appear to be rapidly looking at all the figures, he is actually picking one number, studying it, and leaping on to another.

Unfortunately, analyzing a random or systematic sample of figures can be quite confusing. In random and systematic samples (such as Exhibit 4-7), the confusion stems largely from the fact that the data are usually of several kinds (eight kinds in Exhibit 4-7). Note that if you had, let us say, a list of 40 products and just cost data for these 40 products, a completely random sample might be quite helpful. But when the data are heterogeneous, you may be better off to sample groups or clusters of data which will permit you to make more meaningful comparisons.

Cluster Sampling. Contiguous data are likely to be the easiest to use, provided the report has been reasonably well organized, whereas a completely random sample breaks up this contiguity and for the moment stifles rather than helps insight. (This position will be modified slightly in Chapter 7.)

Exhibit 4-8

PATTERNS OF CLUSTER SAMPLING

a)

	1	2	3	4	5	6	7	8
a	×	×	×	×	×	×	×	×
b	×	×	×	×	×	×	×	×
c	×	×	×	×	×	×	×	×
d	×	×	×	×	×	×	×	×
e	×	×	×	×	×	×	×	×
f	×	×	×	×	×	×	×	×
g	×	×	×	×	×	×	×	×
h	×	×	×	×	×	×	×	×

b)

	1	2	3	4	5	6	7	8
a	×	×	×	×	×	×	×	×
b	×	×	×	×	×	×	×	×
c	×	×	×	×	×	×	×	×
d	×	×	×	×	×	×	×	×
e	×	×	×	×	×	×	×	×
f	×	×	×	×	×	×	×	×
g	×	×	×	×	×	×	×	×
h	×	×	×	×	×	×	×	×

c)

	1	2	3	4	5	6	7	8
a	×	×	×	×	×	×	×	×
b	×	×	×	×	×	×	×	×
c	×	×	×	×	×	×	×	×
d	×	×	×	×	×	×	×	×
e	×	×	×	×	×	×	×	×
f	×	×	×	×	×	×	×	×
g	×	×	×	×	×	×	×	×
h	×	×	×	×	×	×	×	×

Putting the data into blocks and then choosing some of the blocks ensures you a chunk of contiguous data to dig into. Exhibit 4-8 shows several possible patterns of cluster sampling.

Ideally the clusters of data should be as homogeneous as possible from one cluster to another. Obviously the reason for this is that by sampling a few clusters you can get a pretty good representation of what the rest are like. If the clusters were all totally different, you could not do this. For example, suppose that the reports in Exhibit 4-8 contained the type of information given in Exhibit 4-6. In this case, the pattern shown in 4-8 (c) might be preferable, because it would give you clusters in which the same data were reported for each product. This would quickly give you an idea of the kinds of data covered in the report as well as some idea of the range of margins, costs. etc. It is possible to combine the cluster approach with systematic sampling. You would simply set up your clusters and then pick every fourth or every sixth cluster, etc.

Random, systematic, and cluster sampling do not depend greatly on using information that you may have prior to sampling. The sample is not really affected by your ideas and hunches about what may be important. Rather, the selection process is by chance or related to the layout of the figures on the page.

Stratified Sampling. There is an approach to sampling which permits you to use some of your hunches or knowledge in the selection of the sample data. This technique is known as stratified sampling, and involves dividing the data up into groups or *strata* and then choosing a random sample from each. This technique is particularly valuable when you can ensure that the data are quite uniform within a particular stratum and very diverse from one stratum to another.

Most reports are already laid out in some kind of stratified form. For example, in Exhibit 4-6 you may consider the column headings as ways of stratifying the data as they relate to the various products; however, the common groupings in reports are often based on standard concepts or sets of words which may not be relevant to your particular interests at the moment. For example, you may wish to stratify the columns further, and look at a sample of a higher-margin product versus a sample of a lower-margin product, or a high-volume versus a low-volume product.

Other kinds of stratifications, however, are possible beside those brought by the column headings. Again looking at Exhibit 4-6, you might mentally stratify products according to their newness, the amount of promotion behind them, the way they are distributed, or the amount of competition for them. Within each of these stratifications, you could pick a few sample products and look at the data for them. The idea is to form the strata in accordance with characteristics which are of particular interest to you, and then take a look at an example from each stratum. In this manner, you will be sure that the *total sample will contain a representative from each subgroup which is of interest to you.*

SAMPLING INVOLVES IGNORING DATA

Obviously the best way to sample is to know precisely what figures you need and to look only at them. (Stratified sampling involves a modification of this approach.) The point is that it is important to *consciously* ignore irrelevant material which may otherwise clutter up your mind. For instance, a production man looking at the *Nonsense Product Report* may not be interested in dealer discounts and might even go so far as to literally cross out the column so that it would not continue to plague his mind and eyes.

Most reports contain some elements of *redundancy*. This can be very helpful because it gives emphasis and provides means for checking accuracy. Nonetheless, from a sampling point of view, redundancy should be reduced to the absolute minimum; in other words, if you are concerned with reducing the quantity of data, throw out redundant data first.

In Exhibit 4-6, several columns of data can be derived from other columns. Thus, the *net-price* column is simply the sum of the *total-cost* and the *profit* columns. The *list-price* column is the sum of the *net-price* and the *dealer-discount* columns. The *margin-percent* column is a slightly different way of presenting the data in the *profit* column; i.e. it represents the *profit* divided by the *net price*. In a first sampling of this report, it would make good sense to avoid including redundant columns of data in the sample. Thus, if you look at the *total-cost* and *profit* columns, do not bother with the *net-price* column. Include either the *profit column* or the *margin-percent* column but not both.

Actually the notion of redundancy is implied in the general stratification approach. The reason for lumping all new products into a stratum is that you believe new products will behave in a somewhat similar (redundant) manner. Hence you want to pick examples of both new and old products rather than of new products only.

SAMPLING INHIBITIONS

Despite the fact that we engage in sampling of some sort all the time, we may tend to resist the conscious (even though informal) use of it. Many people feel strongly that something must be dealt with in an "all or nothing" fashion. Sampling seems to imply a way of doing things which is neither thorough nor complete. Of course, there is an element of truth in this, but sampling may not be as much of a compromise as you believe. The degree of precision required by the situation must be considered in sampling just as in approximating and summarizing.

At this point, it may be appropriate for you to get some feeling for the power of sampling. The figures cited in Exhibit 4-9, of course, hold true only for the particular situation described. Also, the sampling procedure is handled rather rigorously from a mathematical and statistical point of view.

Exhibit 4-9 [2]

THE POWER OF INFERENCES MADE FROM SMALL SAMPLES

Problem: Estimate average base pay of U. S. Air Force Airmen 2nd Class (A/2C) so that you will be off *no more than 2%* from the true figure.

Question: What number of observations should be contained in a sample to meet the problem conditions 99 out of 100 times?

Answer: (given in tabular form for varying numbers of total Airmen)

Total Number of A/2C	Number of A/2C in sample	Sample size as percent of total
1,000	179	17.9
5,000	209	4.2
10,000	213	2.1
20,000	216	1.1
50,000	217	0.4

The figures should nonetheless suggest the strength of the inferences which can be made even from informal samples.

Exhibit 4-9 shows that given 50,000 Airmen 2nd Class, *sampling fewer than 1% of them* would confirm with 99% certainty that the resulting estimate of their base pay differed from the true figure by no more than 2%.

This example raises the question of how you should go about determining the proper sample size. For the informal sampling discussed here, you do not need to use the somewhat complicated rules of probability. By and large, the *time available and the number of pieces of data which your mind can comfortably handle will take care of determining the sample size.*

Worrying about the inaccuracy of sampling is one side of the inhibition coin; the other side is a feeling that complete analysis is feasible and worthwhile. This is just not always the case. Try counting all the beans in a jar. You will surely not come out with the same total every time. Making even one thorough count will be difficult because you will be bored and your mind will wander. In fact, in many cases, it can be shown that the accuracy obtained from sampling is greater than that obtained from an attempt to take a complete survey. The same phenomenon can occur in attempts to assimilate all the data on a page of numbers. You may understand more by trying to absorb less. There is really no such thing as 100% accuracy anyway!

A data-processing man is likely to point out that you could program a computer to calculate and print out *all* the relevant totals, comparisons, relationships, etc. The problem would remain: someone would still have to sit down and analyze the computer printout, which may run to many, many pages. This does not mean that a computer is not helpful in certain situations. It does not, however, obviate the need for some kind of sampling. (In fact, some fledgling efforts are under way to give the computer some of the businessman's *horse sense* about figures.)

Habit is a further inhibition to the effective sampling of figures. It is just much easier to pick up a sheet of figures and look at the same numbers that you have always looked at; the ones with which you feel at home. Naturally, there are some items (those of particular importance to you) which should be looked at all the time; in so doing, however, you may be ignoring other important sections and messages of the data.

When looking at other sections of the report, try to avoid irrelevant biases such as the three listed below.

a) *Visual convenience.* For example, do not look just at the top or bottom of a column or the beginning and end of a row.

b) *Familiar sections.* For example, when the data are broken down according to geographic regions, do not continually look at only those regions you have visited before and are familiar with.

c) *Good news.* Since most people unconsciously tend to seek out only good news, try to find groups of data which may contain bad news as well. Think about the stocks in which you have invested. Chances are you will first think about the ones which have gone up or on which you made money.

Hunting up new problems and finding new facts are an important part of any businessman's job. Consequently, part of the time you spend thinking with figures should be devoted to exploring data and looking at new areas perhaps with the aid of some random sampling. When you are working with a set of figures, why not try to study at least one group of numbers you have not looked at before (or recently) and try to find at least *one new relationship before* putting down the report.

Many writers on the art of problem solving urge splitting the problem into manageable and meaningful parts. In some sense, sampling can be considered as the same technique applied to figures, because it breaks up data into parts which are easier to cope with than the original mass (or is it mess?) of figures.

A Sample of an Approximate Summary; i.e. a Conclusion

Simplification is essentially a technique of putting numbers in a better form for interpretation, by making the numbers easier for the mind to handle; it provides hooks for the memory and makes it easier to hang the numbers on the hooks; and it reduces the load that the processing unit of the mind must bear.

There is no one master approach for simplifying, since every approach has its own biases and its own losses of information. The techniques of simplification should not be considered as rigorous procedures to be scrupulously followed, but rather as flexible tools to be used in any way that you feel might be helpful.

You may wish that all the numbers you looked at were already approximated, summarized, and sampled for you. This will not always be possible because your particular interests in a batch of figures may change continually. Generally, however, some degree of presimplification is possible. Even if it were possible to completely presimplify figures before you received them, it might not always be desirable. *The process of simplification itself can be an important part of thinking with figures.* Simplification can be a productive means of getting yourself inside the numbers and of becoming aware of the various relationships which require exploration. If you spend a little time putting data in approximate form, taking some totals or averages and selecting a sample, you will suddenly find that you *know* (understand) a good many of the pieces of data and their interrelationships. Even more important, you will find your mind buzzing with thoughts about what to look at next and you will be well on your *figurative* way.

CHAPTER 5

Focusing on Fundamentals

The foregoing processes of simplification help put figures in a form that is easier to cope with and that will stimulate intelligent looking. The next step is to develop some basic ways of looking at these simplified figures, that is, some means of focusing on the important elements.

This chapter is devoted to a discussion of two fundamental concepts: *size* and *comparison*. Practically all the other techniques presented in this book can be viewed simply as alternative tactics for detecting size or uncovering important comparisons.

Sizing Things Up

The bigger something is, the more likely it is to affect the surrounding situation. This seemingly trivial generalization has widespread and important implications. In a business environment, you cannot pay equal attention to everything; rather, you must attempt to single out the important factors and deal first with them.

Because of the manner in which most phenomena are measured, the larger and more important something is, the larger the number it tends to generate. (There are some exceptions to this rule, but it is difficult to think of any good examples.) Thus, in general, large numbers relate to phenomena which could have a significant impact on the firm and may signal important areas for decision, attention, or action.

ABSOLUTE SIZE

If businessmen operated exactly according to the theory of absolute profit maximization, they would worry about saving every penny and cutting waste down to *zero*. It seems that in the real business world, few people rigorously follow such a theory. Executives basically try to achieve a satisfactory return rather than a maximum return. One reason for this behavior is that the pursuit of maximum profit simply becomes too complicated.[1] In other words, some process of selection must be employed.

Most businessmen have "cut-off" points below which they are willing to let things ride. In delegating responsibility, they use the notion of *absolute size,* for instance, only expenditures over a set (absolute) amount would require authorization from a higher echelon.

This same principle can be used when you look at groups of figures. Simply set your own cut-off points. If you are looking at a report of materials purchased, for instance, you might choose to study only those items on which over $10,000 was spent. Of course, absolute sizes will vary from firm to firm, person to person, and report to report.

Size, in fact, is a rather relative concept, and the notion of *relative size* can often be more useful than that of *absolute size;* nonetheless, absolute size has its role to play. A product which produces $1,000,000 in profits is pretty hard to ignore no matter how large the company, since we all have some pretty firmly embedded absolute standards.

RELATIVE SIZE

While relative size may be a stronger concept than absolute size, it is more difficult to extract from the figures. There are, however, a number of techniques that can help spotlight items of large relative size.

Scan by Rows and Columns. Run your eye up and down the columns of Exhibit 5-1 and notice how certain items seem to jump out at you, because they are much larger than the others in the same column. For example, in the column of A-Outlets, the figures 570 and 520 seem quite high in relation to the other numbers, and in the column of B-Outlets, the numbers 2010 and 1695 pop out. Now, 570 and 520 would not have stuck out very much if they had occurred in the

Exhibit 5-1

GADGET CORP. SALES DISTRIBUTION INFORMATION

State	Number of A Outlets	Number of B Outlets	Number of Distributors	Sales ($000)
Alabama	120	220	2	$2
California	440	690	14	30
Colorado	105	160	2	2
Connecticut	75	290	15	35
District of Col.	30	5	1	1
Georgia	160	205	5	16
Illinois	360	960	12	12
Indiana	140	555	1	1
Iowa	120	930	3	16
Kentucky	130	280	1	1
Massachusetts	230	365	17	29
Michigan	270	780	1	1
Mississippi	110	150	2	9
Nebraska	115	490	1	1
New Jersey	160	430	20	24
New York	520	1695	31	93
North Carolina	190	230	1	2
Ohio	265	1090	7	10
Oklahoma	130	250	2	2
Oregon	80	360	1	1
Pennsylvania	355	2010	9	40
Rhode Island	25	105	3	4
Texas	570	590	4	2
Vermont	30	170	2	1
Virginia	130	340	2	1
Washington	140	480	6	16
Wisconsin	225	590	5	18
TOTAL	5225	14420	170	$370

column of B-Outlets. In other words, what seems relatively large in one context may not seem so in another.

This *conscious* scanning of rows and columns for relatively large items is an excellent way of plunging into figures, but rows and columns may not always be equally important. In Exhibit 5-1, scanning across the rows will not be as meaningful as scanning the columns, because each row consists only of heterogeneous items. On the other hand, if the report showed the number of A-Outlets at different time periods, then scanning a row could be quite revealing.

Use Ratios. A ratio is simply a fraction showing the magnitude of any one quantity relative to that of any other. Reducing a ratio to a simpler fraction, for example 24/40 reduced to 3/5, usually pays off in increased clarity. In Exhibit 5-1 look at the sales figures for Pennsylvania and New Jersey, 40 and 24, respectively. Making a ratio would show us that New Jersey sales were 3/5 of Pennsylvania sales. Seeing the relative size in this way may cause you to stop and consider whether or not the relationship is reasonable and whether further investigation is required.

Some ratios, particularly in the financial area, are so frequently computed that they have been given names, *liquidity ratios, turnover rates,* etc., however, there is no special magic in these names or the ratios for which they stand. *The reason for computing any ratio is that it is of interest to you to take a closer look at the size of one number relative to another.* The many varieties of ratios fall into four main types:

a) *Ratios of a part to a part,* e.g. the situation cited above, where sales in New Jersey were compared to sales in Pennsylvania.

b) *Ratios comparing the same item for two different times, places, or situations,* e.g. this year's sales in Pennsylvania related to last year. Sometimes *several items* are lumped together and compared at different times or places. The results are often called *index numbers,* e.g. the common

Consumer Price Index represents the aggregate price of a market basket of certain commodities in one year compared to that in a so-called base year.

c) *Ratios of a part to the whole or total*, e.g. sales in Pennsylvania compared to total sales.

d) *Ratios comparing corresponding parts of different categories*, e.g. the number of distributors in Pennsylvania compared with the sales volume in that state.

Play with Percentages. A percentage is really a special type of ratio: it represents a ratio in which the denominator of the fraction is 100. (*Per cent*, of course, literally means "per hundred.") Any ratio can be converted into a percentage simply by making the denominator 100 and making the numerator correspond so that the resulting fraction will be equivalent to the original ratio, e.g. $24/40 = 60/100 = 60\%$.

Businessmen most frequently encounter percentages as interest on loans or in financial reports of income and expense, but percentages have a much wider application. After all, any two numbers can be made into a ratio and subsequently turned into a percentage.

Several advantages accrue from the fact that in percentages everything is related to the common base of 100. First, categorizing within a standard framework is much easier than remembering diverse kinds of ratios. Second, a standard frame of reference permits easier calculations. Would you rather add $25\% + 45\%$ or $13/52 + 9/20$? (The two sums are equivalent.) Furthermore, 100 is a particularly easy base for calculation.

When you are casting about for a way permitting you to dig further into figures, you can always rely on turning some of the numbers into percentages. This is an excellent technique for flushing out some important relationships or relatively large figures which you might otherwise have overlooked. Exhibit 5-1 indicates that New York has 31 distributors. Since this is the largest figure in the column, it must certainly be considered relatively large. But you get a much clearer insight if you calculate the percentage of the total distributors represented by New York, namely 18%. (This is also easier to grasp than the

Exhibit 5-2

PERCENTAGE OF DISTRIBUTORS BY STATE

State	Percent of Total Distributors
California	8
Connecticut	9
Illinois	7
Massachusetts	10
New Jersey	12
New York	18
	64

bare ratio 31/170.) Since Connecticut has only 15 distributors you might not have paid much attention to it in your first visual scanning of the column. But when you notice that it has $\frac{1}{2}$ as many distributors as New York or about 9% of the total, it becomes more noteworthy. Exhibit 5-2 shows the percentages of distributors for states with over 5% of the total. You can quickly see that six states account for about $\frac{2}{3}$ of the distributors.

As obvious as the importance of size may be, it is daily ignored by countless businessmen. Remember the insidious nature of Parkinson's Law of Triviality: "The time spent on any item...will be in inverse proportion to the sum involved." You will not fall prey to Parkinson's law if you take some time to *size* things up.

Concentrating on Comparison

The notion of relative largeness leads us directly to a most important technique which must be used in conjunction with size to glean the important messages from a set of figures. A number can be considered relatively large or small *only in comparison* with some other number. In order to find the important elements of a group of numbers, comparisons must be made.

It is, of course, mechanically possible to compare any number on a report to any other number on the report or even to a number not contained in the report. The fact that any two numbers can be compared, however, does not imply that the comparison of *any* two numbers will be meaningful. On the other hand, a company is an organism in which almost all the parts are somehow interrelated. It is surprising how many seemingly unrelated numbers do exhibit a relationship when they are compared. Nonetheless, there are certain types of comparison which are more likely to produce significant results.

EMPHASIS ON EXPECTATIONS

The attempt to make sense out of any set of data depends to a great extent on your expectations. Based on your knowledge of the business, previous projections, observations around the firm, past data, etc. you have some idea of what various figures or relationships are likely to be. *You must continuously compare the actual data coming across your desk with what you expect or desire.* It is not a bad exercise every once in a while to go as far as writing down your specific expectations for a figure or report before looking at it.

Some of your expectations will be based on logical patterns like symmetry or consistency. If one expense goes up, you would expect an associated expense to rise (symmetrically). You would expect a figure for sales to agree with the figure computed from the average unit price times the number of units sold; otherwise, the figures would be inconsistent. When comparisons do not confirm your logical expectations, you have cause for investigation. (More about this in Chapter 9.)

Incidentally the value of a budget lies in the basis it provides for comparison with actual figures. Standard costs (often used in budgeting) provide another type of norm (expectation) to be compared with actual results.

Expectations can be important.

DIMENSIONS FOR COMPARISON

If you have in mind some modes of comparison which can easily be related to the types of expectations you have developed, you can raise the odds that your comparisons will uncover something important.

Time. Time appears to be an important element of thinking about the world around you. Note how many of your norms and expectations are expressed in a chronological framework. Thus, *historical* data are often a part of the information flow across a businessman's desk. Forecasts also involve comparisons of current data with projections into future time periods. Comparing fluctuations within a category over time is usually very productive.

Analogous Items. When you compare numbers over time you are really comparing the *same* item recorded at various intervals. The next best thing to comparing same items is to compare *analogous* or *similar items,* e.g. comparing figures on your firm to corresponding figures for other companies (which is why competitive or industry figures are important).

Most firms themselves can be broken down into internal organizational subgroups that have corresponding parts comparison of which would be meaningful. Some commonly useful subdivisions of a firm into comparable groupings are listed below.

a) *Geography.* Comparing the operational figures of one geographical area to those of another can be helpful.
b) *Products.* Every product has sales, expenses, employees, material, etc., associated with it. These form important categories for meaningful comparisons. It is also worthwhile to compare corresponding data for different batches of the same product, and similarly, job orders can be compared.
c) *Operational entities.* Firms can be usefully broken down into such divisions as cost centers, individual factories, etc.
d) *Individuals.* Frequently you will want to compare data relating to individual managers, employees (and shifts of employees), salesmen, or customers.
e) *Causes.* Where figures result from different causes, it can be important to compare the different effects. (For example, Exhibit 7-1 presents the quantity of rejects due to various kinds of failings.

Statistical Bases. Interesting types of comparison may be suggested by the mathematics or statistics of a situation. For instance, you may want to compare an individual figure with some total or average. Thus, financially oriented businessmen might be concerned about what a new project will earn compared with the firm's *average* rate of return. A production man might want to compare the output of a given month with the *average* monthly output over the past year.

Other Categories. There are many other less general dimensions for making comparisons. The list of types of rearrangement given in Chapter 7 should be considered for addition to the above categories.

Of course, data will not always be presented to you in a form which facilitates the kinds of comparison discussed above. This is unfortunate, but should not prevent you from making the important comparisons. In fact, as we shall see in Chapter 7, no matter how excellently a report is laid out, you will always have to do some digging to make important comparisons.

DIFFERENCES

Psychologists tell us that classification is at the heart of our thinking processes, although it is essentially nothing more than thinking about differences or the lack of them (not that finding differences is always easy). There are many types and nuances of differences that can be ferreted out only through the use of elaborate mathematical techniques. In one way or another, however, *comparison is the process used to search for meaningful differences.*

Unfortunately, not all differences are meaningful from a businessman's point of view. Some variations can be caused by chance or inaccuracies in the measuring process. Of course, if these are large, there may be some cause for concern about the measuring process itself. However, some differences are too small to merit the time for investigation. So the question of size is relevant in the search for meaningful differences.

The first category of comparison we discussed was *time,* and naturally it is changes (differences) over a period of time which are important. If factors in the business world stayed the same, a manager's life would be infinitely easier. (Unfortunately, observers of the business scene seem to feel that the rate of change now is greater than it has ever been in the past and is likely to accelerate in the future.) The point is that *change usually shows up somewhere as a difference between two numbers.*

You may want to go so far as to consider looking at *differences between differences.* If sales went up $25,000 in one month (first difference) and up $20,000 the next month (second difference), it could be important to note that the second increase is about 20% smaller than the first one; i.e. sales are going up at a declining dollar rate.

One reason for dwelling on differences is to give you a feeling for how large a part they must play in any attempt to grapple with figures. Furthermore, many areas of calculus and statistics used in sophisticated management techniques have their roots solidly embedded in the notion of differences, and a great many control techniques of management involve the simultaneous use of size and difference.

SIMILARITIES

The dimensions of comparison which reveal differences also reveal similarities (lack of significant difference), but more emphasis is usually put on differences because of their tendency to indicate important areas for management attention. If cost levels were the same for separate factories, you would appear to have little cause for investigation (although admittedly they might be too high or too low).

Similarities become of concern when they are surprises, i.e. when they are different from expectations. You may be upset to find out that sales are the same this year as last year, since they were supposed to grow (or at least you wanted them to grow). Perhaps you expected one division to function more efficiently than another and are curious as to why both divisions seem to be operating similarly.

Knowing that certain items behave in a similar way, i.e. two or more items react numerically to change in the same manner or at least in a predictibly related way, is also extremely useful. Uncovering hidden similarities of this sort is at the heart of many statistical techniques such as correlation and regression analysis, as well as certain sampling procedures. You use this approach informally when you notice that the number of calls a salesman makes seems to relate to the amount of sales produced by that salesman. What you are doing is substituting an item whose behavior is more easily ascertainable for a similar item which is not so easily pinned down. You do this if you look at worker absenteeism and turnover rates in order to assess something about the state of the workers' morale.

This substitutability of similar items is frequently used in forecasting and predicting. For example, your sales may be related to population growth in certain age brackets. Since this population growth can be predicted fairly easily and accurately, you use the projected population figures as a basis for predicting your own potential sales increase.

Conclusion

Searching for sizable items and calculating comparisons are fundamental to analyzing figures. You, of course, have no guarantee that every large figure is truly important or that every sizable difference or unexpected similarity is worthy of investigation. But using these approaches tends to increase the probability that you will perceive what is really important in the numbers. Most of the following chapters suggest other techniques for stimulating perception and further increasing the odds of profitable return for the time spent thinking with figures. But almost all these techniques involve at some point along the way uncovering sizable items or finding meaningful comparisons.

You may have realized by now that thinking with figures requires your *active* participation. Quite often this activity includes *calculations* of some sort which, while useful in other respects, are of direct help in establishing contact with and digging into the figures. Therefore, in the next chapter we shall digress a bit and discuss how you can come to feel more at ease when performing the quick and dirty calculations that can be so helpful. The next chapter may appear to be a digression, but the subject matter is certainly not irrelevant to the art of thinking with figures in business.

CHAPTER 6

Quick and Dirty Arithmetic
for Businessmen

"Speed, it seems to me, provides the
one genuinely modern pleasure."

Aldous Huxley

The Realm of the "Quick and Dirty"

Suppose you decided to hire a public relations specialist to improve your public "numbers" image. The best thing he could probably recommend would be for you to learn a little "quick and dirty" arithmetic. There is no better way of impressing people with your grasp of numbers than to take a problem, make a few rough but lightning calculations, and calmly announce the result while everybody else is still fumbling around getting started.

The inclusion of this chapter might be justified on its public relations value alone, but "quick and dirty" arithmetic is more than a showy gimmick because it does have a real bearing on your ability to think with figures.

All people have a streak of laziness which means that they must overcome some inertia in order to perform any kind of calculation. The easier it is to make a calculation, the less inertia there is to overcome. As you master the art of "quick and dirty" calculation, you will find yourself more and more willing to play with figures in the various ways suggested in other chapters.

Because of the approximate nature of numbers in business, rough calculations can be very efficent and are often all that is necessary. Moreover, as a businessman you cannot escape the need to make calculations, you must develop expectations for comparison with actual figures. You must check reports for clerical and even conceptual errors. The best-prepared reports cannot spare you the inconvenience of making many calculations as you dig into the numbers.

Before plunging into the delights of the topic discussed in this chapter, it may be well to clarify just what we are talking about. The intention is to develop some general principles that will facilitate calculation, as well as a few specific tricks which are useful and even fun. The purpose of "quick and dirty" arithmetic is to free you from the drudgery of long involved calculations. Many of the techniques will increase your capacity for purely mental calculation, but there is nothing wrong with helping yourself by making pencil scratchings.

The goal of this chapter is not to make you into a calculating prodigy or to teach you some esoteric schemes which are useful only as parlor stunts. The emphasis is on some practical shortcuts.

THE "QUICK AND DIRTY" PHILOSOPHY

Approximate results are of primary interest, since quick and dirty arithmetic is basically used where precise answers are not required. Because of this, the discussion is confined to working with numbers of no more than two digits or three at the most. It is simply assumed that you will simplify (at least mentally) all numbers.

Because of this simplification process, magnitude will be ignored until the answer; i.e. what we are most concerned about is the ability to find the first two or three significant digits. If finding the proper magnitude (number of places) in multiplication or division bothers you, the rules and examples of Exhibit 6-1 should clear up most of your problems.

Almost all the techniques which follow have one thing in common: they modify the problem so that the calculations involved are easier to perform. In some cases, this means *simplifying the numbers* to permit an easier calculation, while in others, the technique involves *simplifying the type of calculation* to be done. You should realize that the description of these approaches may make them appear to be cumbersome. Writing down how a mind should think is always a little difficult. Rest assured, however, that the techniques will save you time even if their description seems a bit long winded.

Needless to say, everyone develops his own "quick and dirty" style depending on his abilities. What this chapter offers is really a grab bag of techniques and alternatives which you may meld as you wish into your needs and capabilities.

Exhibit 6-1

FINDING THE ORDER OF MAGNITUDE OF QUICK AND DIRTY CALCULATIONS

Multiplication

To the answer of a multiplication problem simply add a zero for each digit disregarded or dropped in the calculation. In this manner,

24,312		24̶3̶1̶2̶		24
×2,619	simplifies to	×26̶1̶9̶	or	×26
63,673,128				624

The problem of 24 × 26 can be handled by a shortcut described later in this chapter. The question here is whether the order of magnitude of the answer is 624,000; 6,240,000; 62,400,000; or what. To find out, simply note that five digits were crossed out above to effect the simplification. Add back five zeros and you have the proper magnitude for your answer:

624-0-0-0-0-0 or, in other words, 62,400,000.

Division

In division, subtract the number of digits disregarded in the divisor from the number of digits disregarded in the dividend (the number being divided). This gives the number of zeros (places) to add on to the answer:

$$ 2{,}9\cancel{64}\overline{)75{,}0\cancel{27}{,}\cancel{732}} \quad \text{simplifies to} \quad 3\overline{)75} $$

with quotients 25,313 and 25 respectively.

Now	6	(number of digits dropped in 75,027,732)
	−3	(number of digits dropped in 2,964)
	3	(number of zeros to be added on to the answer).

In other words, the approximate division answer is 25,000.

Addition and Subtraction

Do not hesitate to approximate even after you have reduced a column of figures to numbers with two digits. Take Column 1 below,

1)	56		2)	56,231
	39			39,473
	82	might be the simplification of		82,054
	38			38,126
	13			13,398

Run your eye down the *left-hand* digits in Column 1 and add. You will get a total of 20. So you know the approximate total is 200. You can improve this approximation by glancing at the *right-hand* digits. They add to something over 20. Thus, by your "quick and dirty" addition, you might estimate the sum at 220 (or 220,000 for the unsimplified column).

STARTING AT THE LEFT

Most of us have been taught through long years of practice to add by starting at the right. However, for quick calculation, the left is a much more reasonable starting place. First of all, the numbers to the left are really the most important ones in our number system. (As Exhibit 4-2 showed, you lose very little by ignoring the digits to the right.) Moreover, the mind is used to dealing with numbers from left to right. This is embodied in our writing which starts from the left. When you think 56, you do not say six-and-fifty (as in German) but rather fifty-and-six. For quick mental approximation, cultivate the habit of working from left to right. If you write down the procedure used, you will get the following:

```
      56
      39
      82
      38
      13
      ───
      20    (left-hand total)
      28    (right-hand total)
      ───
      228   TOTAL
```

SEPARATION INTO PARTS

A number like 39 can easily be thought of as $30+9$. In fact. this is exactly what thinking from left to right forces you to do. To add 39 to a number it may be easier to add first 30 and then 9. Thus in adding 39 to 56 you would proceed as shown below:

```
      56
    +30
    ────
      86
    + 9
    ────
      95
```

This system can be elaborated into what is known as the "zig-zag" system for longer columns of figures. Thus our column of figures

```
      56
      39
      82
      38
      13
      ───
      228
```

could be added as follows:

$$56 + 9 = 65$$
$$65 + 30 = 95$$
$$95 + 2 = 97$$
$$97 + 80 = 177$$
$$177 + 8 = 185$$
$$185 + 30 = 215$$
$$215 + 3 = 218$$
$$218 + 10 = \mathbf{228}$$

GROUPING BY 10 (OR SO)

The number *ten* is an *easy* number to work with because the zero does not require any handling, except in terms of a decimal place, and the digit 1 is easy to add or multiply. Our number system is based on 10, which accounts for some of the ease in handling this number or numbers close to it. To take advantage of this fact you may want to add a long column of figures as shown below:

$$
\begin{array}{rl}
5 \\
6 & \text{think } 11 \\
3 \\
9 & \text{think } 11 + 12 = 23 \\
8 \\
2 & \text{think } 23 + 10 = 33 \\
3 \\
1 & \text{think } 33 + 7 = 40 \\
3 \\
8 & \text{think } 40 + 8 = 48 \\
\hline
48
\end{array}
$$

ADDITION OF A FIGURE AND LATER SUBTRACTION OF IT

It is perfectly legitimate to add an *extra* number at some point in an addition so long as you remember to subtract it later. The idea is to turn a "hard" number into an easier one by adding something to it. Thus, for example,

$$
\begin{array}{r}
56 \\
+39 \\
\hline
95
\end{array}
$$

can be made easier as follows:

$$
\begin{array}{rl}
60 & \text{(add 4 to 56)} \\
+39 & \\
\hline
99 & \\
-\ 4 & \text{(get rid of 4 added above)} \\
\hline
95 &
\end{array}
$$

This method requires an extra step, but you will find that often these two steps can be accomplished more rapidly than the single one of normal addition. The same trick can be employed if you subtract a number and later add it.

SUBTRACTION

Subtraction is not so complicated as addition because usually you are confronted with only two numbers rather than a whole column. All of the techniques used in addition can be applied to subtraction except grouping by 10's. Thus the operation below.

$$
\begin{array}{r}
56 \\
-39 \\
\hline
17
\end{array}
$$

can be made easier (respectively, by separation into parts or by subtraction of a number and later addition) as follows:

$$
\begin{array}{rl}
\begin{array}{r}
56 \\
-\ 30 \\
\hline
26 \\
-\ 9 \\
\hline
17
\end{array}
\quad \text{or} \quad
\begin{array}{r}
56 \\
-\ 40 \\
\hline
16 \\
+\ 1 \\
\hline
17
\end{array}
&
\begin{array}{l}
\\
\text{(take away 1 more than 39)} \\
\\
\\
\text{(add the 1)} \\
\end{array}
\end{array}
$$

Multiplication

When applying any of the following techniques be sure to use the easiest possible arrangement of the two numbers to be multiplied. After all, it does not really matter which order you use:

$$\begin{array}{r} 89 \\ \times 20 \end{array} \quad \text{is equivalent to} \quad \begin{array}{r} 20 \\ \times 89 \end{array}$$

but the first arrangement lends itself more readily to quick calculation.

APPROXIMATION

Just as in addition, you may find it useful to adopt a slight "devil may care" attitude when multiplying and settle for an approximate answer:

$$\begin{array}{r} 51 \\ \times 24 \end{array} \quad \text{can be thought of as} \quad \begin{array}{r} 50 \\ \times 20 \end{array}$$

The second multiplication can be seen, almost instantaneously, to equal 1000.

There is a worthwhile refinement that can be added to such an approximation procedure: *The numbers being multiplied should be rounded off in opposite directions, with the larger change being made to the larger number.* Thus, if in the example below,

$$\begin{array}{r} 51 \\ \times 24 \\ \hline 1224 \end{array}$$

the 51 is rounded down to 50, then the 24 should be rounded up to 30, so that you will get

$$\begin{array}{r} 50 \\ \times 30 \\ \hline 1500 \end{array}$$

In doing this, however, note that

> you added 6 to the number 24, and
> you took away 1 from the number 54.

In other words, the greater change has been made in the *smaller* of the two numbers being multiplied. The reverse procedure, as said before, is preferable. That is,

$$\begin{array}{rr}
\text{add 9 to 51, which gives} & 60 \\
\text{take away 4 from 24, which gives} & \times 20 \\
\hline
& 1200
\end{array}$$

You can readily see that 1200 is much closer to the exact answer, 1224, than the figure 1500, which came from an approximation that did not follow the suggested rule. There are a few peculiar cases where this rule does not produce the best approximation, but for the large majority it does.

So that this rule will seem a little less arbitrary, let us examine why it makes sense. Rounding in *opposite* directions should seem reasonable; since we distort one figure by making it larger, the obvious way of compensating for this would be to make the other figure smaller. Why, however, insist on making the larger change on the larger number? The basic reason is that a given figure will be a smaller *percentage* of the larger number than of the smaller one; thus the larger number can absorb a greater change with less distortion.

SEPARATION INTO PARTS

As we did in addition, the number 24 can be thought of, by separation into parts, as 20 + 4. The rules of multiplication state that

$$51 \times 24$$

is the same as

$$51 \times (20 + 4) \quad \text{or} \quad 51 \times 20 + 51 \times 4.$$

Thus, working from left to right you would think

51		51		1020
× 20		× 4		+ 204
1020	plus	204	gives	1224

Actually it would have been easier to split up 51, since then one of the multipliers would be 1. In this case, your thinking would be:

24		24		1200
× 50		× 1		+ 24
1200	plus	24	gives	1224

If you had any trouble in multiplying 50×24, you could have performed another separation into parts, this time using subtraction, that is $24 = 25 - 1$. You would just think:

25		50		1250
× 50		× 1		− 50
1250	less	50	yields	1200

There is another type of separation which is frequently helpful. In this case, you look at a number as the *product* of two other numbers rather than a *sum*. For example:

$24 = 8 \times 3$ and 51×24 is the same as $51 \times 8 \times 3$.

Now it is easy to mentally multiply 51×8. Try it! If you have any trouble, just multiply from left to right:

50		8		400
× 8		× 1		+ 8
400	plus	8	is	408

To finish the problem you must multiply 408 by 3. Separation into additive parts will help again:

400		8		1200
× 3		× 3		+ 24
1200	plus	24	is	1224

THE DOUBLE AND HALF METHOD (MULTIPLY AND DIVIDE BY EQUALS)

It is worth pointing out that multiplication by 2 is just about the easiest next to multiplication by 1. Thus factoring a number by 2 is frequently very helpful. In our example, we find that 24×51 is equivalent to $2 \times 12 \times 51$. Thus

$$
\begin{array}{r}
51 \\
\times 2 \\
\hline
102
\end{array}
$$

is easy. However, it leaves the problem

$$
\begin{array}{r}
102 \\
\times 12 \\
\hline
\end{array}
$$

But 12 equals 6×2; so, you double 102 to get 204, which can now be easily multiplied by 6. Working from left to right you can immediately get 1224.

Take another example with a more immediate payoff:

$$
\begin{array}{r}
24 \\
\times 35 \\
\hline
840
\end{array}
\quad \text{is the same as} \quad
\begin{array}{r}
12 \quad (24 \div 2) \\
\times 70 \quad (35 \times 2) \\
\hline
840
\end{array}
$$

TURNING HARD MULTIPLICATION INTO EASY DIVISION

Would you rather multiply by 25 or divide by 4? The two operations are related and often division by 4 is the easier one. Suppose you sold 200 items at 25¢ each. How much money would you have taken in? You might multiply 200 by 25 (this is fairly easy). On the other hand, note that 25¢ are $\frac{1}{4}$ of $1. If the item had sold at $1 each, you would have taken in $200. However, you know that you took in $\frac{1}{4}$ of $200, or $50.

Here is an example where multiplication is much harder than division:

$$
\begin{array}{r}
48 \\
\times 25 \\
\hline
1200
\end{array}
$$

Instead of $48 \times 25 = 1200$ think of $48 \div 4 = 12$ and add two zeros to get 1200. The reason for adding the two zeros is that multiplying by 25 is really the same as multiplying by 100 and then dividing by 4 that is, $25 = 100 \div 4$. Multiplying a number by 100 simply requires affixing two zeroes to the number.

This technique can be used with numbers other than 25. In fact, it will work with any number that divides evenly into 100. For example, multiplying by 50 is the same as dividing by 2 and adding two zeros. Or if you happen to know that 12.5 goes into 100 exactly 8 times, you could divide by 8 and add two zeros instead of multiplying by 12.5. Since there are 12 months in a year, this could be extremely useful in approximations. Often you may want to multiply a monthly figure to see what it would be for a year. Dividing the monthly production average by 8 and adding two zeros will give the approximate yearly figure. For example,

$$\begin{array}{rl} 320 & \text{(units per month)} \\ \times 12 & \\ \hline 3840 & \text{(units per year)} \end{array}$$

To approximate take

$$320 \div 8 = 40$$

and add two zeros to get 4000 units per year.

Some Specialized Multiplication Tricks

Here are some techniques which can be applied only in certain situations; however, they can be used often enough to be worth learning.

PROPORTIONATE FACTORS

Sometimes a number can be split into two helpfully related factors. For example, 33 can be split into $30 + 3$; one factor is exactly one-tenth of the other. Finding one-tenth of a number is done quickly by moving the decimal one place to the left. Consider the following problem:

$$\begin{array}{r} 42 \\ \times 33 \\ \hline 1386 \end{array} \qquad \text{can be done as} \qquad \begin{array}{r} 42 \\ \times 30 \\ \hline 1260 \\ + \ 126 \quad (\tfrac{1}{10} \text{ of } 1260) \\ \hline 1386 \end{array}$$

The same principle can be applied to factors involving subtraction. Look at the following example, remembering that 27 can be broken down into 30 — 3:

$$\begin{array}{r} 38 \\ \times 27 \\ \hline 1026 \end{array} \qquad \text{can be done as} \qquad \begin{array}{r} 38 \\ \times 30 \\ \hline 1140 \\ - \ 114 \quad (\tfrac{1}{10} \text{ of } 1140) \\ \hline 1026 \end{array}$$

This approach also works when the two factors are related by proportions other than 10 to 1, although this one is the easiest to handle. For instance, 48 could be separated into 40 + 8, where one factor is $\tfrac{1}{5}$ of the other or 15 could be factored into 10 + 5, where one factor is $\tfrac{1}{2}$ of the other.

SUMS AND DIFFERENCES

Sometimes, two different numbers can be factored the same way except for a *difference in sign*. For example, take the two numbers 38 and 42:

> 38 can be factored into 40 — 2
> 42 can be factored into 40 + 2.

There is an extremely easy way of multiplying two such numbers. Square the first factor and subtract from it the square of the second. For

$$
\begin{array}{r}
38 \\
\times 42 \\
\hline
1596
\end{array}
$$

think

$$
\begin{array}{ll}
40 \times 40 = 1600 & \text{(first factor squared)} \\
2 \times 2 = -4 & \text{(second factor squared)} \\
\hline
 1596 &
\end{array}
$$

Just to give you another example, take 84 × 76:

84   can be factored into   80 + 4
76   can be factored into   80 — 4.

So you square 80, which you can do instantly, to get 6400 and then subtract 16, which is the square of 4. The rapidly found answer is 6384.

NUMBERS WITH THE SAME FIRST DIGIT AND WITH LAST DIGITS TOTALING TEN

For example, 42 and 48 have the same first digit, and the last digits when added total 10. In a case like this the rule for multiplication promotes extreme rapidity. If you multiply the first digit times itself-plus-one, the result is the *first two digits* of your answer. Then multiply the two last digits. Their product will represent the *last two digits* of the total. The examples below should clarify this procedure: For

$$
\begin{array}{r}
42 \\
\times 48 \\
\hline
2016
\end{array}
$$

think

5	(first digit + 1)		2
×4		and	×8
20	(first two digits of answer)		**16** (last two digits of answer)

To do 73 × 77 in your head just think 7 × 8 = 56, which is the first two digits of the answer. Then think 3 × 7 = 21 and you have the whole answer, 5621.

MULTIPLYING TWO NUMBERS NOT TOO FAR UNDER 100

First, you subtract each of the numbers from 100. The results are called the *complements* of each of the original numbers. Then you add the two complements and subtract them from 100. This gives the *first two digits* of the answer. Finally, multiply the two complements, and you will have the *last two digits* of the answer. Take for example 95 × 94:

the complement of 95 is 100 — 95 or **5**
the complement of 94 is 100 — 94 or **6.**

```
   100
 —   5                      5
 —   6                     ×6
 ─────                    ────
    89   (first two digits  30   (second two digits
          of answer)               of answer)
```

Thus 8930 is the full answer.

The two figures need not both be in the 90's. The procedure would work equally well with a problem like 97 × 82, where the complements would be 3 and 18, respectively:

```
   100
 —   3                     18
 —  18                    ×3
 ─────                   ────
    79   (first two digits of answer)   54   (second two)
```

So 7954 is the full answer.

MULTIPLYING BY 11

To find the answer, simply add the two digits of the number to be multiplied by 11 and insert the result between these two digits. Thus for

$$\begin{array}{r} 32 \\ \times 11 \\ \hline 352 \end{array} \qquad \text{take} \qquad \begin{array}{r} 3 \\ +2 \\ \hline 5 \end{array} \qquad \text{place the 5 in the middle} \quad 3\ \mathbf{5}\ 2$$

If the sum of the two digits is more than 10, just carry the 1 and add it to the first digit. For

$$\begin{array}{r} 49 \\ \times 11 \\ \hline 539 \end{array} \qquad \text{use} \qquad \begin{array}{r} 4 \\ +9 \\ \hline \mathbf{13} \end{array} \qquad \text{then} \qquad \begin{array}{r} 4 \text{ - } 9 \\ \mathbf{1\ 3} \text{ -} \\ \hline \mathbf{5\ 3\ 9} \end{array}$$

Remember that all the foregoing approaches can be applied to numbers that only approximately fit the criteria for a particular technique. For example, 43 × 48 is close to 42 × 48. The latter problem can be handled exactly by the rule for two numbers with the *same first digit and last digits totaling 10.* The quick answer is 2016, which you know will be close. (If you want to be precise, remember that the number 2016 will be off exactly 1 × 48 which you can add to get 2064.)

Division

Division does not lend itself to rapid calculation if exact answers are needed. One of the main problems is that most divisions produce remainders. Nonetheless, if you are willing to accept rough or approximate results, then most of the techniques used in multiplication can be appropriately modified for division.

APPROXIMATION

Rounding off numbers can be just as easily done for division as for multiplication, but the rule for compensating is a little different. *Both the divisor and the number being divided should be rounded off in the same direction, so that the greater rounding is done to the number being divided:*

$$143 \div 37$$

should be rounded to

$$150 \div 40 \qquad \text{rather than} \qquad 140 \div 30.$$

You can estimate the answer to $150 \div 40$ by thinking that 4×40 would be 160 while 3×40 would be 120. So the answer must be slightly less than 4 (perhaps 3.9 or 3.8). Just go ahead and guess, for even if you said 3.6, you would not be too far off from the accurate answer, 3.84.

SEPARATION INTO PARTS

Just as in multiplication, you can break the number you are dividing into two parts. For example, the number 294 can be thought of as $300 - 6$. Look at the following problem on this basis:

$$294 \div 3$$

can be thought of as

$$300 \div 3 \quad \text{less } 6 \div 3 \qquad \text{or} \qquad 100 \quad \text{less } 2 = 98.$$

This technique is most useful when the divisor is a single digit or a single digit followed by zeros, for example, 6 or 600.

When the divisor has several digits you may want to break it up into factors: For example, 16 can be thought of as $\mathbf{2} \times \mathbf{8}$. You would then proceed as follows:

$$336 \div 16$$

can be thought of as

$$336 \div \mathbf{2} = 168, \qquad \text{and then} \qquad 168 \div \mathbf{8} = 21.$$

Exhibit 6-2

ROUNDED DECIMAL EQUIVALENTS OF EASY FRACTIONS

0.50 = 1/2	0.20 = 1/5	0.12 = 1/8	0.91 = 1/11
0.33 = 1/3	0.17 = 1/6	0.11 = 1/9	0.83 = 1/12
0.25 = 1/4	0.14 = 1/7	0.10 = 1/10	

TURNING HARD DIVISION INTO EASY MULTIPLICATION

This is just the reverse of what was talked about in the corresponding section on multiplication. Thus, dividing by 25 is equivalent to multiplying by 4 and taking away two places. Dividing by 50 is equivalent to multiplying by 2 and taking away two places. For example 300 ÷ 25 can be thought of as

$$
\begin{array}{r}
300 \\
\times 4 \\
\hline
12\cancel{00}
\end{array}
$$
(cross out two places)

It is, in general, easier to multiply than to divide; so this technique has a much broader application here than in the previous section on multiplication. The table of decimal equivalents in Exhibit 6-2 will suggest further uses for turning *hard* division into *easy* multiplication.

For instance, consider the problem 408 ÷ 17 which can be thought of as

$$
\begin{array}{r}
408 \\
\times 6 \\
\hline
244\cancel{8}
\end{array}
$$
(cross out two places)

Fractions

By and large, the best way of dealing with fractions is to convert them into their decimal equivalents as shown in Exhibit 6-2, where the decimals are approximations. The fact of the matter is that most of the figures you are presented with in business will be stated as decimals rather than fractions. Remember that the same techniques apply no matter where the decimal point appears; that is, the same approach for multiplying by 25 can be used in multiplying by 2.5 (which is the same as $2\frac{1}{2}$). Multiplying by $5\frac{1}{12}$ is about the same as multiplying by 5.83 (which should probably be rounded to 5.8). All the approximation procedures discussed in this chapter should definitely be applied to dealing with fractions.

Conclusion — The Importance of Spot Checking

A businessman must continually verify and check the figures he sees, if only to catch clerical errors. There have been actual cases of plants being mistakenly shut down because of a misplaced decimal point. In addition to catching errors, the businessman who is thinking in figures should be continually playing with numbers in an approximate way, making estimates, and exploring new possibilities in rough numerical terms. Making exact calculations is an exacting and tiring job.

The art of "eyeballing" involves rapid scanning of figures to catch their implications, and an important part of "eyeballing" is making some "quick and dirty" spot checks to locate errors.

Look at the following column of figures:

$$
\begin{array}{r}
4,325 \\
6,478 \\
2,194 \\
2,683 \\
5,731 \\
\hline
41,411
\end{array}
$$

One way of spot checking this addition would be to run your eye down the *left-hand* column, perhaps grouping by 10's. That is, you see the 6 and the 4 and think 10 and notice that the rest

of the numbers make 9 for a total of 19. There is quite a difference between 41 and 19. It is large enough to make you suspect
that the sum of the numbers in the next column will be too
small to account for the difference. You suspect an error, and
of course there is one, since the correct total is 21,411.

Or let us say you multiply 56 × 84 and obtain 4703. By
looking at the product of the two units digits, you see that the
exact answer must end in a 4, since 6 × 4 = 24. You conclude
that some sort of error must have been made. Or suppose you
see the multiplication 15.4 × 4.32 = 665.28. You should reflect
mentally that the answer must be somewhere near 15 × 4, or
60, which is a long way from 665.

Admittedly, these examples are not very complicated, but
they are typical of the kind of errors which continually crop up.
Even though the spot checking involved is fairly simple, there is
no better way of developing your "quick and dirty" ability.

It would be only fair to point out that rapid calculation is an
art and, like so many other arts, requires practice. Fortunately,
it is not like the mastery of the piano or violin which requires
setting aside so many hours a day for practice. The world of
numbers is all around you. Thus you have a chance and perhaps
an obligation to practice every time you think with business
figures. You may also enjoy practicing apart from business. For
instance, the next time you go to the supermarket, or eat in a
restaurant, use "quick and dirty" arithmetic on your bill. Clerks
and waiters do not always make mistakes in your favor. Thus,
besides improving your abilities, you may receive a nice dividend for your efforts. If the mistake is in your favor, then you
have a moral problem which it is up to you to resolve.

Oh yes, do not forget to practice at meetings with your employees or other businessmen. If you make an error, nobody
will think much of it since it was only supposed to be a rough
estimate, but if you come out reasonably close, you will be
well on your way to establishing your reputation as a "numbers expert."

CHAPTER 7

Developing The Habit of Change

"All things in change do delight"

John Donne

Habit and Change

Take a quick look at the three phases in Fig. 7-1. Now look away from the page and see whether you can repeat them exactly as they are printed. Did you do it? Are you sure? Maybe you had better check again. Perhaps you should look at the phrases and read them off one word at a time. Even after all this checking and looking, some people still do not notice that the words *and, the,* and *a* are repeated in the circle, rectangle, and triangle, respectively.

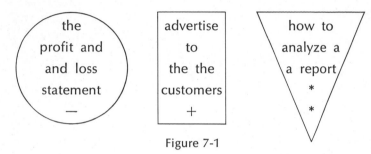

Figure 7-1

Most people who have not seen the demonstration before miss at least one of the duplications. This is simply a dramatic illustration of how your habits of looking can get in the way of your seeing what is really there. When something falls into a well-known or familiar pattern, your perceptions tend to follow that old comfortable pattern. You see what you think you should see (or in some cases what you would like to see).

These same perceptual limitations can develop in the handling of numbers. Suppose that you receive a particular report week after week or month after month, and that the format is always the same. You simplify it, look for sizable figures, make comparisons, etc., but you always look at the same subsection of the report and end up comparing the same numbers. Suppose further that one day somebody important walks in and asks whether you had noticed a particular item that was inexplicably large (especially in comparison with some other figures). You would be forced to admit (at least to yourself) that you had never really noticed this important and surprising state of affairs.

Consider the diagram in Fig. 7-2. What designs and patterns do you see in it? You may not realize that all the digits from zero to nine as well as all the letters of the alphabet can be traced out within it. In fact, light bulbs that are arranged in precisely this array are used on billboards to show the time or flash news headlines.

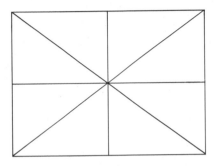

Figure 7-2

So it is with a group of numbers. There are a great many patterns waiting to be uncovered, some of them important, some of them not. It is difficult to force your mind to seek out new patterns, much less cover all the old patterns you already know.

In some cities, there are subway or bus stations with large maps showing the many possible intersecting routes. If you push the proper button on a panel listing various destinations, the route for your chosen destination lights up on the map. This chapter can not claim to set up any comparable lightboard for numbers. However, it does suggest some techniques which can help illuminate new relationships and some approaches which will shake up your old habits of looking at figures.

Change is the common ingredient that gives potency to the techniques of this chapter. There are quite a few varieties of change that can induce new number insights. First, there is *rearrangement,* which does not change any individual number, but does change the *order* or *spatial relationship* of numbers on a page. Second, it is possible to *restate* a number or a group of numbers in different units of measurement. Third, you can actually *change the value* of one number to see the effect on other figures. Fourth, there is *translation* of numbers into some other language or symbolism.

Rearrangement

In his *Rules for Direction of the Mind,* Descartes states that, "Method consists entirely in properly ordering and arranging the things to which we should pay attention." Over the centuries, the technique of rearrangement has continually had advocates in many diverse fields. Rearrangement in the hands of the cubist painters created controversy. They would take the elements of a chair (legs, seat, back, etc.) and completely rearrange them, creating some new, if perturbing, perceptions of chairs—as well as painting. Rearrangement has been used to capture attention. For instance, advertising men continually seek unusual new arrangements of well-known objects: e.g. a siren selling cigars to a shipwrecked sailor on a desert isle. And rearrangement has been used as a method of attack in solving complex scientific problems as well as lowly anagrams.

A rearrangement of any of the phrases in Fig. 7-1 would have immediately signaled the presence of the duplicated word:

statement
and loss
the profit
and

Let us see how this concept might apply to the figures of the Gadget Company. Let us assume that the Inspection Report

Exhibit 7-1

GADGET CORP. INSPECTION REPORT ON REJECTIONS BY TYPE OF DEFECT

Defect Type	Number of Pieces Rejected				
	Mar	Feb	Jan	Year to Date	Last Mar
Off-center hole	11	22	25	58	12
Bad coating	57	18	21	96	45
Bad scratches	19	29	17	65	30
Bad weld	43	37	41	121	39
Off size	18	45	46	109	26
Low spring tension	10	15	8	33	5
Rough edges	35	9	12	56	37

shown in Exhibit 7-1 has been used for quite a while. The layout permits easy comparison of the figures accumulated this month with those of last month. Spend a few minutes scanning the report in Exhibit 7-1 to see what messages you can extract. Now let us find out whether your insight increases as we rearrange the report.

First, suppose we rearrange only the March figures according to their relative size (Exhibit 7-2). Note how this arrangement

Exhibit 7-2

MARCH REJECTIONS BY RELATIVE SIZE

Defect Type	Number
Bad coating	57
Bad weld	43
Rough edges	35
Bad scratches	19
Off size	18
Off-center hole	11
Low spring tension	10

Exhibit 7-3

REJECTION REPORT REARRANGED PER EXHIBIT 7-2

Defect Type	Mar	Feb	Jan	Year to Date	Last Mar
		Number of Pieces Rejected			
Bad coating	57	18	21	96	45
Bad weld	43	37	41	121	39
Rough edges	35	9	12	56	37
Bad scratches	19	29	17	65	30
Off size	18	45	46	109	26
Off-center hole	11	22	25	58	12
Low spring tension	10	15	8	33	5

immediately highlights the categories of *bad coating, bad weld,* and *rough edges*. In fact, these three categories account for almost 70% of the total defects.

Suppose we rearrange the whole report in this new order as in Exhibit 7-3. Now compare March with February. It is easy to see that the relative size of the categories differs greatly between the two months; i.e. bad coating and rough edges were not among the prime causes for rejects in February whereas they were in March. The power of rearrangement, however, is not yet exhausted. This time let us change the position of the columns as in Exhibit 7-4.

This rearrangement permits easy comparison of year-to-date figures with those for March. Again we find that bad coating and rough edges are not so important in the year-to-date figures as they are in March. Comparing this March with last March, we find that the order of importance is exactly the same. There is a strong implication that something special is happening every year in March. Perhaps the climate or temperature is causing excessive rough edges and bad coating in March. On the other hand, bad weld seems to be a continuing problem of some magnitude.

Exhibit 7-4

REJECTION REPORT REARRANGED AGAIN

	Number of Pieces Rejected		
Defect Type	Year to Date	March	Last March
Bad coating	96	57	45
Bad weld	121	43	39
Rough edges	56	35	37
Bad scratches	65	19	30
Off size	109	18	26
Off-center hole	58	11	12
Low spring tension	33	10	5

BASIC TECHNIQUES OF REARRANGEMENT

Exhibits 7-1 through 7-4 illustrate some of the basic techniques of rearrangement. Most reports are set up with rows and columns of figures. You can rearrange the rows as in Exhibit 7-3, i.e. switch around the elements of a column, or you can easily change the order of the columns as was done in Exhibit 7-4. Thus, changing the order of rows or columns is an easy and very productive technique of rearrangement.

The implication is not that the arrangements of the numbers in Exhibits 7-2 through 7-4 are better than those found in the original report. They are simply, in a helpful way, different. Unfortunately, arranging the figures by size in March means that the relative sizes are jumbled for the other months. Similarly, putting the cumulative column and the column "Last March" on either side of the March column for the current year (Exhibit 7-4) makes it harder to compare March with February.

It is not fair to say that one arrangement is as good as another. *It is important to distinguish between order and tidiness,* i.e. between rearrangements which lead to important insights and those which simply put the figures into a neat pattern. Of course, if you have a little extra time on your hands, moving the figures around any which way could lead to some interesting arrangements. It would probably be more efficient, however, to rearrange the numbers according to some specific criterion which you suspect will produce meaningful new insights.

What are some of these generally useful categories or criteria? The importance of size was discussed in Chapter 5, and we have already used size in rearranging the Rejection Report of the Gadget Company. *Size* is typically a high priority basis for re-arrangement.

Chronology (or *time* as it was discussed in Chapter 5) is another obvious basis on which to rearrange figures. You may feel that most reports tend to be laid out in some kind of chronological order. Do not forget though, that chronology has many dimensions. You may want to compare this month with last month or the month before, or the year-to-date figures, as well as with the same month in a previous year. It is geometrically impossible to lay out a report format that will permit all these comparisons to be made with equal ease.

The other categories mentioned in Chapter 5 can be used as a basis for rearrangement, but in addition you might want to consider the following rearrangement possibilities.

Customary Order. Arrangement is often determined by custom, such as male coming before female. Following custom is a convenience but by itself does not tend to produce useful arrangements.

Alphabetical or Numerical Order. Items are arranged according to the order of the alphabet or the order of a numerical progression. Employee data could be listed alphabetically by name. If machines are identified by number, then data pertaining to them could be listed in numerical order. These arrangements permit you to readily locate particular items, since you know precisely where they will fall in the sequence of listed data.

Natural Order. Certain series of items have a natural or logical order to them. A product in process may travel from coating, to cutting, to polishing, etc. Geographical segments may form a smooth progression from east to west. Items might be arranged from immediate to remote or simple to complex.

Some other bases for rearrangement spring from important management concepts. These usually encompass two poles or extremes. Data can be arranged along the dimension which runs from one extreme to the other.

Repetitive and Nonrepetitive Aspect. This might involve, for example, segregating repeat customers from newly acquired customers or separating one-time costs from recurring costs.

Controllable and Uncontrollable Cases. Data may refer to things you control, or items beyond your control, or perhaps beyond the control of the firm, or to things attributable only to chance. Certain costs may be imposed upon you by suppliers, while others may be controlled by your efficiency. You may want to consider the notion that *sunk* costs represent money already spent and therefore not under control, whereas *incremental* costs represent money not yet expended and therefore controllable.

Direct and Indirect Cost. Some data apply directly to a specific item. Others apply to a group of items and cannot be exactly allotted. For instance, supervisory time cannot always be directly assigned to a specific product or activity. The cost of lighting can be applied only indirectly to specific people or products.

Fixed and Variable Costs. Certain data apply to elements of the firm that are relatively permanent, e.g. the area of the plant, the amount of heavy machinery. Other items are more likely to be variable, e.g. the number of employees or the number of hours worked.

REARRANGEMENT EXTENDED

Physical separation makes it difficult to see relationships and make comparisons. For instance, copper and tin can be fused to form durable tools of bronze. Evidently, this was a difficult discovery for Stone Age man to make, because copper and tin are not usually found in the same place.[1] It is difficult for the eye and mind to relate things which are not close together. The ancient Greeks mentioned *contiguity* as one of their three laws

Exhibit 7-5

TYPICAL REPORT FORMAT

	a	b	c	d	e
A	×	×	×	×	×
B	×	×	×	×	×
C	× ←--× ←— ☐× —→× --→×				
D	×	×	×	×	×

of association. (The other two, *similarity* and *contrast,* were discussed in Chapter 5.)

Take the typical report format shown in Exhibit 7-5. As you can see, any one number can have a maximum of four close neighbors (even fewer if it is in a corner). As the eye moves away from the numbers immediately surrounding a particular figure, it becomes more than proportionately difficult to see relationships clearly.

This difficulty is greatly magnified when the figures to be compared are on separate pages, especially if the pages come from different reports. But there is no reason why the techniques of rearrangement could not be extended to numbers appearing on different pages of different reports.

After all, a business is an organism, and what happens in one of its parts is quite likely to have some effect on many others. As an exercise to prove the point (and develop your number ability), take any two reports that you receive and see what possible connections there might be between them. You will find it hard to choose two reports which cannot be correlated in some meaningful way to permit new insights.

Putting together parts of different reports can be just as important at other levels as at the top of a corporate organization. Most supervisors, at any level, receive numerous reports which relate to their functional areas and which are likely to merit rearrangement. A sales supervisor, for instance, may want to check salesmen's expense reports against reports showing the orders landed by each salesman. A production man may wish to relate rejection rates to machine processing speeds.

Of course, top management is expected to put together information received from more than one functional area. Sales reports should be reviewed alongside of production reports. You might discover that production had been highest in the product line for which sales had been lowest, a relationship which certainly could not be permitted to continue indefinitely. The point is that production is tied in with purchasing and sales; personnel turnover and salaries have a relationship to production costs and efficiency. Research and development activities tie in with sales efforts, and so on. In fact, it is interesting to speculate whether departmental managers as well as lower-level supervisors, might not profit from examining a few relevant reports from areas other than their own.

Putting together reports may seem terribly obvious and logical. Indeed it is; yet the mind of even the most aggressive executive is sometimes lazy. It takes consious effort to flip your eyes and thoughts back and forth from one page to another; even more so when this means digging into two separate files. But the rewards for such effort can be very great.

THE NEED FOR REARRANGEMENT

Rearranging numbers does not change their individual values. So, in theory, any insight made after rearrangement could have been discovered beforehand. Some businessmen do, in fact, develop the ability to perform a lot of mental rearranging. Most people, however, find that using pencil and paper is a necessary adjunct to efforts of this kind.

Often when a particularly fruitful rearrangement is uncovered, you may wish to formalize it into a new report. Remember, though, that no matter how cleverly you design a report, you will always be confronted by new situations arising for which your arrangement will not be appropriate.

Some psychologists claim that the real essence of problem solving is finding a connection between formerly separate things. Perhaps some day, someone will invent four-dimensional paper (or paper with an even greater number of dimensions) which will enable you to really put a figure "next" to all the other figures with which a comparison might be worthwhile. Until such time, rearrangement will continue to be an important tool for digging into numbers.

Changing Units of Measurement

The Phantom Tollbooth is a delightful bit of educational whimsy written for children by Norton Juster. Milo, a little boy, and the Humbug, his traveling companion, at one point in their adventures, come upon an enormous road sign reading:

DIGITOPOLIS
5 miles
1600 rods
8800 yards
26,400 feet
316,800 inches
633,600 half inches
AND THEN SOME

"Let's travel by miles" advised the Humbug, "it's shorter."
"Let's travel by half inches," suggested Milo, "it's quicker."[2]

This bit of banter may seem foolish, for of course we grown-ups know that all those figures say exactly the same thing. It really does not matter which expression we use—or does it?

Suppose that the only thing on the sign had been "1600 rods." The chances are you would not have had a very good idea of the distance to Digitopolis. You are probably not accustomed to thinking in the unit of measurement called *rod*.

Suppose the only thing on the sign had been "633,600 half inches." You should have a fair idea of the length of a half inch. Yet the length 633,600 half inches does not convey a very clear idea of the distance to Digitopolis. The problem is that your mind encounters difficulty in finding an appropriate image with which to compare 633,600 half inches. Thinking in inches is only good for relatively short distances.

Probably the indication "5 miles" is the most meaningful one, because we are used to thinking of long distances in terms of miles. We can refer to stored experiences of such distance and the quantity "5" is not too hard to grasp.

THE IMPORTANCE OF UNITS OF MEASUREMENT

One reason for selecting certain units of measurement is to make the numbers involved of a magnitude easily grasped by the mind. Primitive tribes had trouble differentiating quantities greater than 3 or so. We have trouble with only slightly larger numbers. When an astronomer tells us that a star is trillions of miles away, the figure does not convey much more than the notion of "very large distance." We try to express large numbers in a way that makes them more comprehensible. Someone describing a large, wild Hollywood party graphically stated, "If all the people at that party had been stretched out end to end— I wouldn't have been surprised!"

The mind tends to work in units that by custom or convenience have become the standards for one or the other given situation. We pile up a backlog of experience recorded in terms of certain units of measurement. When data are presented in other than these customary units we may find it harder to see all the implications. Suppose you are used to seeing your firm's net profit as a percentage of *gross* sales. One day your new controller starts computing the percentage using *net* sales as the base. You are no longer sure how to interpret the percentage since it is difficult to relate it to your backlog of experience. When your favorite stock splits, the chances are you multiply the new stock quote by the split factor to get a figure comparable to the old quotes stored in your mind.

So you may change units of measurement just to fit them to your habitual background. On the other hand, you may change them in order to break up this traditional frame of reference and thereby force new perceptions. It is interesting to note that many contests offer trading stamps as prizes. This means they can talk about *"millions* of trading stamps" as prizes instead of just *"thousands* of dollars."

WAYS TO CHANGE UNITS OF MEASUREMENT

Changing the Size of the Units. In general, this involves making the unit of measure a good deal larger or smaller. Suppose someone comes to you with a proposition that may add ten minutes of productive time per day. This may not seem like much to you. If you had been told, however, that this scheme would add over a week of productive time each year, you might have felt differently. Suppose it is proposed that a bonus of $20 be paid to each employee each year. This seems like a modest enough sum, but in terms of 600 workers this would mean $15,000 a year, every year. Maybe such a bonus proposal needs further consideration.

Here are a few other examples illustrating the breaking down of the unit of measurement. Many companies require salesmen to report the number of calls made. So the sales supervisor may find himself looking at a report showing that a salesman made 960 calls in a month. Breaking down that figure would give an average of 10 minutes per call (assuming an eight-hour day and no time for transportation). Analysis using this figure might yield clearer insights than that using the figure of 960 calls per month. Suppose that one of your machines produces 240 pieces in a given week. By changing units, you can show this to be equivalent to 6 pieces an hour or one every 10 minutes. You

If 1 man can paint a house in 12 days, could 96 men do it in 1 hour?

can then more easily visualize the machine in operation and perhaps reach some conclusion about whether or not 10 minutes per piece is reasonable.

Sometimes you can use a combination of increasing and decreasing units. For example, if you are told 1 man can do something in 12 days, could 12 men do it in 1 day or 96 men in an hour? You might not want to push this so far as to suggest that 1,038,000 men could do it in 1 second.

The use of ratios and percentages, discussed in Chapter 5, could also be considered as a type of change which produces new insight.

Changing the Type of Units. There are many techniques of measuring a particular phenomenon. Remember that since measurement is a kind of description, it is always partial and incomplete. Thus, a different type of measurement of the same phenomenon is likely to provide a different slant. For instance, most people think of sales as the sum of sales of individual products or individual plants. However, it might turn out to be interesting to think about sales per dollar of investment or sales per labor man hour. To take another case, a production man might want to convert idle machine hours into units of production lost.

Frequently it can be advantageous to change a measurement into dollars. If you notice that a product is out of stock 10 times a month, you could try to remeasure this in terms of dollars of business lost. An average turnover figure for employees could be remeasured in terms of dollars of training and experience lost. Putting figures into dollar terms permits them to be compared with the wide array of other dollar figures available. In fact, one important reason for changing the type of units of measurement is to facilitate comparisons. This applies to many other common units of measurement as well as to dollars. Airlines, for example, for purposes of totaling and comparison, convert all of their flight data into passenger-miles.

One particular type of change in measure is a bit unusual, namely, *transfer*. It involves taking measures which are used in one area of business and seeing whether they would have any meaning when transferred to a totally different area. For instance, financial men talk about measures of liquidity, i.e. the ease with which a firm can obtain excess cash. Would the concept of liquidity have any analogous meaning if a personnel manager were to apply it to his department? Might it perhaps be his ability to supply needed people readily? A production man is often concerned about the quantity of rejects. What would the concept of rejection percentage mean if transferred to the sales department? Perhaps it could have something to do with the number of sales not consummated? The use of transfer as a means of generating meaningful new insights has been largely unexplored. Perhaps you now have some feeling for the creative possibilities of this technique.

Changing One Number to See The Effect on Other Numbers — The What-If Approach

A business firm represents a body of interrelated activities. A change in one of these activities is likely to affect a whole range of other activities, which in turn affect other parts of the company. The figures which represent these activities possess much the same organic quality. As a rule, changing one figure on a report leads to a change in a number of other parts of the same report or other reports.

Making hypothetical changes of this sort is the basis for many financial techniques used in business management. A *pro forma* (projected) balance sheet is nothing but the result of assuming some changes and seeing what their effect will be on various balance sheet items. Similarly, you can assume an increase in sales and see what the effect will be on your costs and ultimate net profit.

The point is that this technique is applicable to figures other than those appearing on financial statements. In the previous section we discussed looking at the output of a machine in terms of minutes per piece. Suppose you decide that the operation is taking twice as long as it should. What would happen if you assumed that the operation were changed so that it would take half as long per piece? You would not necessarily double your output. It is possible that the next operation is already functioning at full capacity and that you would have to incur extra costs to handle the additional output. On the other hand, you might be able to make do with fewer machines and perhaps use some of the workers elsewhere. Even if the time per piece seemed reasonable, you still might indulge in this flight of fancy to see just how important a reduction in production time per piece could be.

Suppose that you were looking at the Sales Distribution report of Exhibit 5-1. You might be interested in seeing what would happen if you increased your number of distributors. The new distributors might sell some merchandise, but the existing distributors might sell a bit less. Then of course you might have to increase the number of salesmen in order to service the new distributors, and so on.

Working out the implications of a hypothetical change like this will help you see where improvements might be made. Often, a slight change will have a great effect because of the chain of consequences it sets off. Conversely, sometimes a great change will not have very much impact at all on the overall picture. Playing with numbers in this way will give you an idea of where it would be advantageous to make real changes. But just as important, as you play with the figures you will gain a much deeper understanding of how they are tied together. This in turn will lead you to a better understanding of how the resources you manage are interrelated.

Do not be surprised if you find it difficult to complete one of these hypothetical excursions. You may have to pick up the phone to ask questions of somebody else or you may lack certain information necessary to make reasonable assumptions. This is to be expected and can play an important part in improving your knowledge of the firm's operations. As was pointed out in Chapter 2, one of the important by-products of looking intelligently at figures is the discovery of important questions to be resolved and new information to be searched out.

This "what if" kind of approach has been outlined in the field of business creativity by people such as Alex Osborn. If you are interested in this approach, you may want to read some of Osborn's books and develop a list of "what if's" for yourself. This list would include such approaches as widening or narrowing a situation, increasing or decreasing quantities, assuming that a situation is more or less serious than it really is.

Working with hypothetical situations provides a double benefit: You find out something about the *hypothetical* situation itself, and at the same time, you uncover a great deal about the *actual* situation (numbers) which is confronting you.

Translating Numbers into Other Languages

"In learning any foreign language, you form new concepts, you discover relationships you didn't realize before, innumerable nuances, similarities, differences enter your mind; you get

Exhibit 7-6

GADGET CORPORATION OUTPUT INFORMATION

a) Month	Units of Output
January	20,000
February	22,000
March	24,800
April	28,700
May	34,200

b)

J   F   M   A   M

c) $Output_n = 140\% (Output_{n-1}) - 6000$

d)   Each month since January output is higher than the previous month. The rate of dollar increase seems to be steadily increasing.

a rounded view of everything. Which means that you think differently in every language . . ." So spoke Schopenhauer, the German philosopher.

Earlier chapters have referred to the *language* of numbers. Perhaps then, it would not be amiss to see what translating numbers into other languages might mean.

In Exhibit 7-6 (a) some monthly figures for output are given. These same figures are then expressed (or translated) into three other "languages." In 7-6 (b) the language of geometry and graphics is used. The chart permits you to visualize the magnitude of the figures and their relationship to each other. Graphs permit you to make some comparisons which might otherwise be difficult to make. Graphs are even more useful when you are comparing two sets of numbers, e.g. output compared to sales over a given number of months. Some people just like to draw pictures; they understand them better than cold, unadorned numbers.

Item (c) in Exhibit 7-6 uses the language of algebra. The equation states that if you take 140% of the output of the previous month and subtract 6000 units, you arrive at the output of the present month. Putting the data into this sort of formula can help you project future months (if you believe the future will follow the present trend). The equation is just a description of the line in the chart, but it is sometimes easier to work with equations. Equations scare the numerical pants off of some people, whereas others do not feel that they have really grasped a set of figures until they have been able to reduce them to some kind of formulation. Nevertheless, when the mathematics really gets tough it may be easier to play with a graph; for instance, you can join two points on a chart without using any mathematics.

Item (d) simply describes the output figures in words and sentences (many alternative verbal descriptions would have been possible). Using words helps clarify some of the meaning in the figures. Many people find words more soothing than stark figures or charts.

Which of the langages is better? There is no answer to this question. Much depends on your abilities and preferences. The important point is that different *emphases* emerge from the different languages. Items (a) through (d) are *not* simply redundant presentations of the same material. Even if you are comfortable with figures alone, you may want to perform a few translations. Looking at numbers in a new language will rarely fail to give you new insights.

Moreover, the *process* of translation is excellent for helping you to feel at home with a set of figures. Even before you start to analyze your translation, you will already have a good feel for the import of the figures and ideas about paths for further exploration. Translating into a new "language" provides an important and dramatic type of change—a sure way to break up your habitual view of things and whet your appetite for insight.

Perhaps the magic of *change* can best be summarized by the paraphrase of an old saying:

Change and your whole world changes with you.

CHAPTER 8

The Art of Informal Higher Mathematics

Talk about sophisticated mathematical techniques for business use is in the air. You can hardly pick up a business periodical without seeing something about such topics as *linear programming*, PERT, *game theory, simulation,* or *probability theory.* Unfortunately these subjects abound with jargon as well as a good bit of mathematics—a rather ominous combination. Even their titles seem esoteric and tend to intimidate the average person. Many businessmen are afraid of becoming bewildered and so are inclined to ignore these techniques or to assume that a specialist can be called in when these techniques are needed.

No doubt, the sophisticated application of these advanced concepts must be carried out in part by experts with specialized training and experience. This does not imply by any means that the average businessman can escape scot-free. In the first place, somebody has to know when to call in the expert. In other words, someone has to recognize that a situation may be susceptible to the application of one of those advanced disciplines. Second, experts must always rely to some degree on data and other information provided by businessmen. Frequently, the mathematical expert is not so expert in the business affairs with which he finds himself involved. In any given situation, some businessman must know enough about the mathematical techniques to assure the expert that the proper data are being collected and used.

There is a third, all-pervasive, reason why businessmen cannot afford to be unaware of the new mathematical approaches. *These new techniques—apart from any mathematics—usually involve new and important ways of thinking about business problems.* Advanced techniques often suggest new categories for making observations, new ways to organize people, or new approaches to decision making. To put it another way, many formal mathematical notions have informal interpretations which can be of use to the executive in his everyday encounter with business problems. These advanced mathematical techniques can provide interesting frames of reference through

Higher mathematics can have an informal everyday use.

which to view business situations without necessarily getting into any sophisticated calculations.

At some time or another, you have probably run your eye across a series of figures showing how some entity has behaved over a long period of time, e.g. figures showing the amounts of various raw materials purchased for each of the past five years. In scanning such figures, you are informally using an approach known technically as *time-series analysis,* a collection of techniques which when formally applied requires complicated calculations.

Another time, you may have glanced at monthly sales figures and compared them with the monthly profit figures to see whether they vary in the same way. In doing this, you are informally applying a technique known as *correlation analysis*—another complex mathematical, statistical technique.

In earlier parts of this book we discussed the informal use of other advanced concepts as an aid to dealing with figures.

Chapter 4 discussed *sampling*, and Chapter 5 mentioned taking a quick look at the *dispersion* of a group of numbers. Both concepts play an important part in advanced statistics.

It would be impossible within the scope of this book to cover all the major mathematical techniques now applied to business. This chapter, however, presents, in some detail, a few of them primarily to show what new perspectives they can bring to everyday dealing with numbers. The approach will be to briefly describe each technique, using practically no mathematics and to emphasize a feeling for the kinds of problems for which the technique is useful. Equal attention will be given to highlighting the significant informal notions that can be developed out of the techniques.

Models are discussed first because they are at the heart of many advanced mathematical approaches and may shed light on techniques discussed elsewhere in this book. In particular model building is a part of both *simulation* and *linear programming*. Widespread publicity has been accorded to these two techniques. As a result, they are, at the least, important topics of cocktail-party conversation about which any successful businessman should have some knowledge. In all fairness, it should be added that the notoriety of simulation and linear programming is justified since both formally and informally they have application to a broad range of business situations.

The Magic of Models

Models, quite simply, are representations of real life objects or situations which are easier to deal with than reality itself and are used to gain insight into the things they are supposed to represent. Models are often thought of as primarily *small* physical replicas like a toy train, but physical models can be life size or even bigger. You have probably read that the astronauts take many simulated trips in mechanical models of their space capsule long before they ever leave the earth in their real rocket-powered vehicles. Physical models (both two- and three-dimensional) are often used in planning the layout of a new plant.

Pictorial models are also quite common. A topographic map is really a model. Engineering drawings of a product can also be considered as a kind of model. Graphs and charts may even be thought of as pictorial models.

We will be primarily concerned here with mathematical and statistical models. An equation showing the relationship between demand for a product and the price of the product would be considered as part of such a model. Some models attempt to represent a situation at a given point in time. Others, more dynamic in nature, attempt to represent situations over a series of time periods.

BUILDING MODELS

Essentially *models are analogies or abstractions* of a real-life situation and, as such, inevitably are a simplification of reality. Therefore, *models must always omit something.* If a model contained everything that was present in the real situation, it would be as complex and difficult to handle as the real situation itself and would be of no benefit.

At the same time, a model is not successful unless it somehow manages to capture the essential elements and relationships of the real situation. A model of plant operations that assumed laborers would work a straight eight-hour day (no idle time, no rest periods, no late arrivals and not even any coffee breaks) might not produce information that would correspond with the real life situation.

So, building a model involves *selection* of key factors and relationships. This process requires careful attention to the objectives for which the model is to be used. Let us use as an example the demand for elevators in an office building (since we will be using the same example in talking about simulation later on). The purpose of the model will be to give us some insights about the length of time that passengers are likely

In building a model it is difficult to unearth all the important factors.

to have to wait before an elevator arrives. In building the model you would try to exclude extraneous considerations such as the kinds of clothes worn by passengers (unless women's fashions go back to the hoop skirt days and thereby affect the number of passengers an elevator could hold). On the other hand, pertinent information such as times of coffee breaks and lunches could be very important, since they would cause high demands to be placed on the elevators at certain times.

Sometimes it is very difficult to unearth all the important factors which complicate a situation. Pile-ups at elevators are affected by the speed of the elevators, the capacity of the elevators, the number of elevators, the time it takes people to get on and off, the number of people waiting, how long they have been waiting, and many other factors.

You must learn those things about the key factors that you wish to work into the model and uncover how the key factors behave and interact. Often what you learn from constructing the model may be just as worthwhile as what you learn from using it.

You may have to pore over historical records, e.g. maintenance records for the elevators might show how often and for how long they were out of commission. Perhaps you will have to take some actual sample observations, e.g. watch the passengers arriving at the elevators to determine the traffic pattern. In many other cases you may have to be content with some reasonable guesses about the behavior of the various factors.

Correctly constructing the actions and interactions of the factors in a model is just as important as proper selection of these basic factors. It is these built-in interactions which allow the model to respond and react to the various experiments performed upon it.

Informal Model Building. How can you make informal use of model-building concepts? First, you should consider the importance of *substitution*. Using a model involves substituting something simpler (the model) for something more complex (the real situation). This technique can be used countless times in the daily conduct of a business. The techniques of approximation, summarization, and sampling discussed in Chapter 4 all involve informal substitution. In fact, a model really is a type of approximation or summarization. It is even possible to consider numbers themselves as models, since they represent only selected aspects of a much more complex real situation.

Constructing a model forces you to choose the important elements of a situation and to look at the various interrelationships. Chapter 3 emphasized the importance of knowing explicity why you are looking and what you are trying to find out. Chapter 7 suggested the use of rearrangement and several other techniques to bring out new relationships between various numbers.

In fact, there are many situations where it may be worthwhile to construct a rough model, even if you do not spell out all the relationships in a precise quantitative way. Let us suppose that you are thinking about ways to increase the productivity of a salesman. You may first try to isolate the factors that have an important effect on his productivity, e.g. his experience, his compensation, other incentives, his territory, his supervision, the product and its price, packaging, etc. You might also try to establish some of the basic relationships between these factors. For instance, compensation may depend somewhat on territory and years of experience. The selling price may affect commission incentives. Just the exercise of constructing this model (even if you do not use it thereafter) can greatly help to clarify your own thinking. Moreover, most of the current research in problem solving seems to point to the importance of developing a *search model* (or *anticipatory scheme* as it is sometimes called).[1]

TESTING THE MODEL

After constructing a model, the next step is to test it, i.e. to make as sure as possible that the model adequately represents the real situation. There are two principal checks which can be applied informally as well as rigorously.

The first is to simply stand off and look at the model as a whole. Does it seem reasonable? Are there internal inconsistencies? For instance, in the elevator example you might find the model indicated that at lunchtime there would be more people waiting on one floor than the number of people working in the whole building, or you might find the model implying that many people were going to the washroom on the 4th floor but not returning (possible but highly unlikely at least for any prolonged time period).

The other kind of check involves trying out the model on some historical or sample data to see how closely it comes to generating observed data. Suppose you had records of the demand for the elevators at different hours of the day and also actual data showing the waiting times at these hours. You could submit the demand data to the model and see whether the waiting times produced were reasonably close to those on record.

An obvious but often overlooked point is that the data used for testing should not be the data used in developing the model. Exhibit 8-1, an illustration of this simple but often ignored point, presents a chart with many points. You are to attempt to construct a line (model) that represents the general trend of the points. You decide that points A and B if joined would produce a pretty good general trend line (model). You would not then test the accuracy of such a line by seeing whether it passed close to those *same* points. Instead you would have to check several *other* points, such as C and D, to see how far off they were from the trend line (how will they fit the model).

To recapitulate: Your informal models should be scrutinized for reasonableness and consistency. (Certain aspects of this kind of checking are discussed in the next chapter.) And they should be checked to see whether they correctly predict or produce data which you already know (but did not use in constructing the model).

With this understanding of models, we now turn to *simulation* and *linear programming,* techniques where models play a significant role.

Simulation

The dictionary definition of the verb "to simulate" is "to assume the appearance of, without the reality; to feign." In some ways this is not a bad capsule description of the business technique known as simulation. (Business simulation, however, does not have the somewhat derogatory connotation of feigning or concealing the truth.) In simulation, you create a model as a representation of a piece of the real world (capturing the

Exhibit 8-1

CHECKING A MODEL

a) Here are some data in graphic form on sales volume related to number of salesmen.

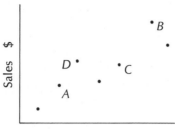

b) You construct a trend line.

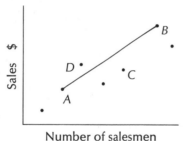

c) You check the trend line by looking at points other than A or B.

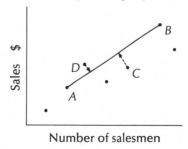

true nature of the situation as closely as possible) and then study the way this model behaves under various conditions.

Almost everyone has used his imagination to perform an informal sort of simulation. You may have imagined a meeting you were to have with someone, say a negotiation or a job interview. Or you may have imagined how a particular piece of countryside might look at different times of year. Perhaps you have tried to visualize how a new package for your product will look when the merchandise is placed in a store for sale.

Your imagination and powers of visualization are limited, however, and situations can quickly become too complicated to think through in your head. Try your powers of imagination on this simple puzzle: Suppose that you have a sweater with a label inside the collar at the back. If you turn this sweater inside out and put it on with the left arm in the right sleeve and the right arm in the left sleeve, where will the label be?

If this sweater problem makes you a little dizzy, your first impulse will probably be to run and get an old sweater. Following the directions with an actual sweater would show you that the label ends up on the outside at the back of the neck. Your decision to hunt up a sweater would be a sound one. If you can think through a situation, using real-life actions, then there is little need for simulation. For instance, one way to see how a new package would look in a supermarket would be to walk to a nearby supermarket and place the package on one of the shelves.

Many situations, however, do not lend themselves to real-life tests. Barriers of time, money, and other resources may prohibit such experimentation. For instance, it would be impractical as well as expensive to buy a new machine, install it, train people to use it, etc. just to find out whether it would increase production by the desired amount.

Mathematics is often resorted to when real-life experimentation is not feasible. If you wanted to know the level of sales at which you start to make a profit, you might set up an equation of costs and revenues and solve it to find the so-called

Exhibit 8-2

A SAMPLING OF SIMULATION SITUATIONS

---

1) To decide whether the addition of another elevator will sufficiently reduce passenger waiting time for elevators

2) To investigate the effectiveness of switching to centralized scheduling in a company with multiple sales offices, mills, and warehouses

3) To help decide whether to embark on a promotional campaign in view of its effects on demand, plant capacity, costs, etc.

4) To compare a new inventory policy with an existing inventory control system

5) To help an oil company forecast quantity and quality of output by simulating a whole refinery

6) To analyze how various types of congestions affect the output of a plant

7) To determine the costs of various forms of product guarantees

8) To determine the most efficient layout of runways at an airport

9) To decide on the number of repair mechanics to be assigned to maintenance for a group of automatic machines

10) To help determine how many warehouses a company should have and where they should be located

---

break-even point. When you solve an equation, you are using a *direct* mathematical procedure which produces a solution. You may be just a little pleased to learn that the power of mathematics to solve problems in this way is a good deal more limited than you might have thought. There is a large class of problems which cannot be solved by direct application of a mathematical procedure because the necessary mathematical concepts have not yet been discovered. There are also many cases where a problem could be solved by direct mathematical procedures but the method would be so involved and lengthy as to be too cumbersome and impractical to apply. In these cases, simulation may turn out to be of help.

Thus simulation is the technique to be used when an experiment cannot be made in the *real* world, and when a direct mathematical process does not exist or cannot be efficiently applied. In essence, then, simulation is a kind of indirect mathematical procedure which involves experimentation. It is hoped that the reults of the experiments can be used to obtain the desired solution to a particular problem.

The situations listed in Exhibit 8-2 are just samples of the many kinds of business problems for which simulation has been used. You can see that it has been applied to evaluate proposed changes in a great many functional areas of a business. As a matter of fact, it has even been used to analyze whole plants, an entire business, and in some cases problems involving an entire nation.

THE PROCESS OF SIMULATING AND ITS VARIOUS USES

When you simulate with a model, you act upon it in some way, i.e. you provide an input. The model, taking this into account, eventually produces some response, that is it generates some output. Let us look briefly at Example 1 in Exhibit 8-2. You first build (and test) a model that does a good job of determining waiting time for elevators. You feed it, as an input, a hypothetical additional elevator. The model already contains information and relationships pertaining to the demand for the elevators. Using this framework, the model now incorporates the presence of an additional elevator into its equations and spews forth information on the average waiting time with the additional elevator.

Note that what a model produces is not an answer as such but rather data comparable to those which might be produced by a real situation. The procedure of constructing a model and using it to produce data is the heart of simulation. In the case of the elevators, the simulation does not tell you directly how much waiting time would be decreased by the addition of the extra elevator. Rather, the model generates waiting time data for the hypothetical situation with the extra elevator running.

You could cause the model to generate such data for the equivalent of one day. (This job might take a computerized model only a few seconds.) Or you might prefer to get data for a year or more. Then it would be up to you (or your mathematical aide) to take the data and analyze them to discover just how the presence of the extra elevator might affect waiting times.

Thus, simulation provides a method for experimentation and testing answers. It is not a method for directly providing the best answers or final solutions. For instance, in the elevator problem, you could easily simulate data for two additional elevators instead of one, or for elevators with larger capacities or different operating characteristics. It is this flexibility which makes simulation so useful. Even if it were feasible to put in an elevator on a trial basis, it would surely be impossible to try different elevators and test them for long periods of time.

Another use of simulation involves exploring the effect of changing assumptions or relationships within the model itself. In the case of the elevators, you may want to know the effect of staggering lunch hours or of installing a washroom on each floor.

Informal use of simulation can provide some of the same advantages. In your informal model of a salesman's productivity, you could play around with his compensation to see how much more he would have to sell to warrant an increase. You might mentally raise the price of the product to determine how the extra revenue produced could be put toward a salary increase. Something of this technique was used in Chapter 7, where it was called the "What-If-Approach." There is definitely an element of playing around in both formal and informal simulation. If you knew how to get the answer directly, you would do so. Instead, you must propose various possibilities and see what happens. Then, on the basis of these projected results pick the best answer.

Simulation also is a very important way of getting a feel for a situation; i.e. it helps you determine what factors are crucial and how sensitive they are to other elements of the system.

You might find, for example, that the average waiting time for elevators is affected very little by substantial increases in the total number of people in a building. This conclusion comes not from solving an equation or going out to observe the real world but from first generating and then analyzing simulated data produced by a model.

You were able to understand and describe the various components of the model, but soon it became so complicated that you could not mentally or mathematically see the *overall* effects, i.e. you could not predict exactly how the model would behave. As a result, you were forced to learn the behavior of the model by feeding it data, letting it process the data, and then looking at the results.

There is no reason why an informal try-it-and-see process cannot be used to great benefit. Take a look again at the salary problem in Chapter 2 concerning a raise twice a year instead of once a year. Now, you could set up an equation that would tell you exactly how much the two wage systems would differ over any given period of time. On the other hand, if you lacked the skill to set up such an equation, you could easily do what was done in that chapter, i.e. work out (simulate) some samples. The numbers in Exhibit 2-1 represent an example of such informal simulation. You can look at the sample figures and draw some fairly obvious conclusions about wages under the semi-annual compared to the annual system.

It should be pointed out that simulation is used for many purposes other than business situations and is being applied to many fields other than business. One interesting application has been in games. Management games have been developed to give training and insight into marketing, production, the stock market, national defense, etc. Less complex versions are being sold in many toy stores. In fact, one could consider "Monopoly"* as a type of simulation game, and it has been around since the 1930's. Maybe its success indicates that simulation

---

* Trademark.

using a model based on the throwing of dice and the picking up of arbitrary instruction cards does bear some relationship to life in the real business world.

Linear Programming

Linear Programming (LP) deals with problems involving the most efficient allocation of scarce resources to interdependent uses, i.e. problems which require your examining alternative ways of using resources in order to achieve a desired goal. Basically an LP problem has two parts: first, some measure of the goodness (optimality) of a particular allocation of the resources and second, a set of conditions (constraints) which the factors in the problem must satisfy in order that the solution be a feasible one.

In LP, just as in simulation, you set up a model of the situation. If the model is of a particular type, then an LP procedure can be applied which will ultimately yield a solution, i.e. the LP procedure will guide you through successive steps to the optimal allocation of the resources. In Exhibit 8-3, you will find a brief tabulation of some typical problems for which models susceptible to LP can be constructed.

Of course, all these problems could also be explored by simulation. In fact you may notice a similarity between the allocation example in Exhibit 8-3 and Item 10 in Exhibit 8-2. Simulation permits you to try out all sorts of arrangements but gives you no idea whether the next one will be any better than the one before. So you may have to experiment around quite a bit before you hit upon the right set up. Although LP does not lead you immediately to the best solution, it does guarantee that each trial will be an improvement over the preceding one and thereby reduces greatly the number of trials it takes to uncover the best solution.

Exhibit 8-3

COMMON CATEGORIES OF LP PROBLEMS

Problem Type	Measure of Goodness	Constraints
Allocation. Assigning the output of several plants to a number of warehouses	How low is the total freight cost?	Warehouse requirements and capacities Plant capacities and outputs Freight rates
Blending. Dog food	How low is the total cost of the ingredients?	Costs of ingredients Vitamins, calories, etc., per unit of each ingredient Quantity of vitamins, calories, and amounts of meat, cereal, etc. required per unit of the finished dog food
Product Mix. What products should be produced on a number of different machines?	How much profit can be obtained?	Number and type of machines available Machine capacities Product profit margins Minimum quantities of the various products to be produced

More situations are susceptible to simulation than to LP. Nonetheless, LP has been used in a wide range of areas, e.g. selection of advertising media, make-or-buy decisions on manufactured components, and choice of alternative investments.

A MEASURE OF GOODNESS

Another look at Exhibit 8-3 should help clarify what is meant in an LP problem by a measure of goodness. This concept is relevant to your everyday dealing with figures and business problems. You should have some measure of goodness in mind whenever you attempt to judge a situation or decide between alternatives. However, all too often the measure of goodness is not made explicit. This can lead to confusion and troubles in verbal or numerical communication. Often alternative measures of goodness or a combination of various measures may be appropriate. For example, when you think about investing in a new machine, do you want the cheapest machine that will do the job? Do you care about the risk that the machine will become obsolete? How important is the length of time that the machine will last? It is difficult to come to an intelligent conclusion unless you develop a clear idea of your measure of goodness.

CONSTRAINTS

Furthermore, LP forces you to become very explicit about the constraints within which you must contain your thinking. In an actual LP problem, the constraints must be quantified so that they can be written in the form of equations. It may be well for you to formalize your own thinking about any problem to this degree. You may find that something you thought of as a restraint is, in fact, not a restraint. You may find some new constraints of which you were not aware.

For instance, if you wish to increase production, are you limited by one-shift operations as a restraint or is it possible to go two shifts? Must you reach your goal without adding new machines, or can you buy or lease additional ones? Are you limited by the union agreement? There is not much point in thinking up solutions which do not fit the constraints imposed by the situation.

While we are on the subject of constraints, it may be appropriate to point out why the word "linear" appears in the term "Linear Programming." In mathematics, linear relationships are those which can be represented by a straight-line graph, i.e. when two factors have a linear relationship, they vary together in some directly proportionate fashion. If a workman earns $2 an hour and his wage varies linearly with time, you would expect him to earn $16 in an eight-hour day. Now, if he works over eight hours, his hourly rate changes because of overtime premium. Thus his total wage for a *ten*-hour day would not have a linear relationship to his wage for a day of *eight* hours or less.

In an LP problem, in order for the mathematics to work, all the conditions and restraints must involve linear relationships. This is not the important point for our discussion. In our informal thinking with figures, it can be very important to think about whether or not a set of numbers varies proportionately with something else. To cite an example, the production cost per piece of Widgets may increase proportionately as volume increases unless such quantities are desired that an extra machine must be purchased, or a new plant built. Many items which appear at first glance to behave in linear fashion do not, or perhaps they do so only within narrow limits.

Inequalities. The restraints of an LP problem are typically written in the form of inequalities; e.g. you cannot produce *more than* a certain amount at a given plant or you must have *at least* so many vitamins in each pound of dog food. This can be a useful little trick to remember when you are dealing informally with the restraints of a situation. For instance, suppose that you have a given number of machines to be used in production. The restraint is that you cannot use *more* than you have, but remember that you do not have to use *all* of them.

Thinking in terms of inequalities may open up possibilities you had not thought of before. A curious property of many LP solutions is that they indicate that certain seemingly valuable resources should not be completely used. In a product mix problem, for instance, an optimal LP solution might show that a very productive machine should be left idle part of the time or run at less than full capacity.

In fact it may be important at times in your everyday thinking to *consider the nonuse of a resource as an explicit entity*. Linear Programming problems handle this mathematically by introducing a so-called *slack variable* which is used to turn a restraint expressed as an inequality into one expressed as an equality. You introduce something to represent the amount of *unused* capacity. Then, instead of saying you cannot produce *more than* a certain amount at a given plant, you may say that the used capacity plus the unused capacity *equals* the total capacity. Take the case of vitamins in dog food. You might introduce a factor to represent the amount of extra vitamins (which of course might be none). Then instead of saying you must have at *least* so many vitamins per pound, you could say that the amount of vitamins per pound less the extra vitamins *equals* the required amount of vitamins per pound.

SETTING UP AN LP PROBLEM

Typically, the data in an LP model are displayed in a matrix form such as the transportation allocation problem illustrated in Exhibit 8-4. (Many management reports tend to be laid out at least partially in this way.) This layout forces you to

Exhibit 8-4

MATRIX LAYOUT OF A SAMPLE LP ALLOCATION PROBLEM

Warehouses	Production Plants			
	Chicago	St. Louis	Cleveland	TOTAL
Cincinnati				5,000
Des Moines				7,000
Detroit				4,000
Minneapolis				10,000
TOTAL	11,000	6,000	9,000	26,000

Exhibit 8-5

MATRIX LAYOUT FOR FREIGHT RATES IN LP ALLOCATION PROBLEM

Warehouses	Production Plants			
	Chicago	St. Louis	Cleveland	TOTAL
Cincinnati	$4	$5	$3	
Des Moines	5	4	10	
Detroit	2	8	3	
Minneapolis	6	8	11	
TOTAL				

consider combinations and relationships which you might not have looked at before. For example the table in Exhibit 8-4 helps you realize that the St. Louis plant can indeed ship to any one of the four warehouses, whereas in the past you may have had a tendency to think only in terms of the closer warehouse.

By the way, the totals in the table indicate the restraints and conditions, e.g. the Cincinnati warehouse cannot handle more than 5000 units and the Chicago plant output is 11,000 units. The example has of course been simplified by making the total output of the plants equal to the total storage capacity of the warehouses. The problem here is to decide which plant should ship to which warehouse and in what quantity. The best arrangement, naturally, depends on the prevailing freight rates (laid out in matrix form in Exhibit 8-5), e.g. it cost $4 per unit to ship from the Chicago plant to the Cincinnati warehouse.

The matrix layout is a very important technique for dealing formally and informally with figures. It might actually be classified as a type of rearrangement like those discussed in Chapter 7. Even when data are presented to you in one matrix form, you may want to pick different categories with which to create a new matrix. Drawing up a matrix forces you to

Exhibit 8-6

POSSIBLE SOLUTION TO THE LP ALLOCATION PROBLEM

Warehouses	Production Plants			
	Chicago	St. Louis	Cleveland	TOTAL
Cincinnati	[4]	[5]	[3] 5,000	5,000
Des Moines	[5]	[4] 3,000	[10] 4,000	7,000
Detroit	[2] 4,000	[8]	[3]	4,000
Minneapolis	[6] 7,000	[8] 3,000	[11]	10,000
TOTAL	11,000	6,000	9,000	26,000

Total Freight Cost = $141,000

pick two types of classification (one for the rows and one for the columns) and concentrate on the cross relationships between them. Laying out the data in such cross-classified form shows you clearly what data are missing, permits you to see patterns in the data, and suggests new approaches to the situation at hand.

SOLVING AN LP PROBLEM

Once the LP matrix of conditions and constraints is set up, there are several technical methods for solving the problem most of which involve two common elements. First, you must construct a possible solution, i.e. one that fits the conditions and constraints, even though it is probably not the optimal solution according to the measure of goodness. For instance, in Exhibit 8-6, a possible solution to the allocation problem of Exhibit 8-4, the entries tell you how many units are being shipped from a particular plant to a particular warehouse.

Note that the row and column totals fit the total unit constraints as given in Exhibit 8-4: the various shipments to Cincinnati do not exceed the 5000 unit storage capacity there.

Of course, the real problem is the freight cost for all the shipping. Since Exhibit 8-5 gave us the unit cost for various routings, we can cost out the suggested allocation of Exhibit 8-6. The small numbers in the brackets simply represent the freight cost per unit. In other words, the freight data from Exhibit 8-5 have been transferred into the brackets of Exhibit 8-6. To get the total freight cost we simply multiply the number of units by the freight cost per unit shown in the bracket. For example, 5000 units are to be shipped from Cleveland to Cincinnati at a cost of $3 per unit or a total cost of $15,000. Next we add the totals in each cell and obtain a total freight cost of $141,000.

The second common element of all LP methods consists of some techniques to arrive at an improved allocation such as the one shown in Exhibit 8-7. There the total freight cost, $120,000, shows a significant improvement over the first solution. We would continue to apply this LP procedure as long as each new trial yielded an improvement, i.e. a lowering of cost. At some point the LP procedure would tell us that we had arrived at the minimum cost, i.e. that there were no possible changes that would lower the cost further. In the problem we have been using as an example the minimum cost would be $116,000.

Informal Trial Procedure. The moral of all this seems clear: there is nothing wrong with making intelligent trials. (If it is good enough for LP, it should be good enough for every day informal use.) In particular, it is important to *make a start somewhere, even though you know you are not starting with the best approach.* All too often you may hesitate to dig into figures simply because you are not sure that you are doing exactly the right thing. The previous chapters have presented various surveying techniques. None of them guarantees that you will get to the heart of the figures immediately but they

Exhibit 8-7

FIRST IMPROVED SOLUTION SUGGESTED BY LP PROCEDURE

Warehouses	Production Plants			
	Chicago	St. Louis	Cleveland	TOTAL
Cincinnati	[4]	[5]	[3] 5,000	5,000
Des Moines	[5]	[4] 6,000	[10] 1,000	7,000
Detroit	[2] 1,000	[8]	[3] 3,000	4,000
Minneapolis	[6] 10,000	[8]	[11]	10,000
TOTAL	11,000	6,000	9,000	26,000

Total Freight Cost = $120,000

do provide methods of starting, and of roaming around the numbers in an intelligent fashion.

For the sake of our informal methodology it is worth taking a closer look at the heart of the LP procedure, that part which indicates how to improve the allocation. In LP, we examine the given allocation to determine what kind of switch would provide the greatest improvement. Let us go back for an example to the trial solution of our transportation problem, Exhibit 8-6. Suppose that we decided to ship one extra unit from Chicago to Des Moines. Of course, this one unit will have to be taken away from some other routing out of Chicago and that change will require another change, and so on, so that all the conditions of the problem are still satisfied. Each of these changes will have a cost effect, i.e. not shipping a unit over a route previously assigned saves money while shipping an additional unit over another route increases cost. Listed below are the various cost effects and the necessary re-routings that arise from shipping that extra unit from Chicago to Des Moines:

one unit from Chicago to Des Moines . . . . costs $5,
one less unit from Chicago to Minneapolis . . . . . saves $6,
one more unit from St. Louis to Minneapolis . . . costs $8,
one less unit from St. Louis to Des Moines . . . . . saves $4.

The total effect is a net increase in cost of $3. Therefore shipping a unit from Chicago to Des Moines would not be an advantageous re-allocation. Linear Programming essentially permits you to quickly review possible re-allocations to see which one would be most advantageous. After making one improvement you can inspect it again via the LP mechanism to determine whether further improvements are possible.

Let us jump back to our informal point of view. Looking at the results of even a slight switch in the allocations of resources can be a useful approach even without using rigorous mathematics. A marketing manager may want to consider how much sales would increase if he took a certain amount from the advertising budget to hire another salesman, or, perhaps, to develop a better package instead. A personnel man may wonder whether worker satisfaction might be improved if he devoted more time to careful recruiting or if this might require too much of a sacrifice in the amount of time spent on worker training and so on.

You may even want to put some numerical values into your thinking as you play around with hypothetical re-allocations. You might estimate that a new salesman would produce $100,000 worth of sales. You would then have to consider whether reducing the advertising budget by his salary would cut into sales more than this $100,000.

THE DUAL OF AN LP PROBLEM

All LP problems have a related problem, known as a *dual*, which uses the same data as the original problem but is concerned with different relationships. The *dual* focuses on restraints and conditions of the original and examines the costs or values imposed by these restrictions. For instance, in our example of freight allocation, one of the constraints involved the output of each plant. The dual problem would be concerned with the value or effect of releasing the restriction on output, e.g. how would increasing the output of the Chicago plant by one unit affect freight costs (assuming that production at some other plant were reduced by one unit). Similarly the dual problem would deal with the effect of changing the capacity of a given warehouse so that more could be shipped from the various plants.

Informal Thinking about Releasing Constraints.   Again this type of thinking can be extremely valuable even when applied informally. Any time you are dealing with a situation where there are restrictions, it is well to remember that releasing them will have a value or effect. Releasing different restrictions produces different values. It is worthwhile considering the different alternatives.

If you have a production situation where the men and equipment you can use are fixed, but you know that eventually you will have to change these restrictions in order to increase production, you would want to examine the relative dollar value of increasing your manpower as opposed to getting better machines. In other words, restraints are necessary because most resources are scarce and consequently valuable. Thus various scarce resources (evidenced by restraints) should be analyzed and compared to see which has the greatest value. Then, when the opportunity arises to modify the restraints, you will know which one is limiting your profits the most.

To summarize a bit, at the root of many business situations lies the problem of allocating scarce resources to alternative uses so as to maximize output or minimize cost. Linear Programming suggests some helpful methods for examining these allocation problems. The dual of an LP problem emphasizes the importance of investigating the relative scarcity (value) of the resources involved in order to determine which restraints it would be most valuable to release a little.

Higher Mathematics — Formal and Informal

You have now been conducted rather quickly and hopefully in comfort, through the complicated techniques of simulation and linear programming and their use of models. Hopefully you can and will make frequent informal use of the ideas suggested by these advanced management techniques. As a fringe benefit, you may have found that these sophisticated techniques were not as "far out" as you might have thought. At least some of the mystery and strangeness has been removed from them. Perhaps you will be impelled to find out more about other valuable mathematical techniques now that you realize that you can comprehend them.

The mind, with all its mysterious powers, does have limited capacities. Linear programming and simulation, like so many other techniques, are called into play when the unaided mind cannot handle the complexities of a real-life problem. These advanced formal techniques have been developed to solve this overload problem, just as many of the informal methods presented in this book will help you to overcome the overload problems you face in dealing with pages of numbers.

CHAPTER 9

Creative Report Looking

Thinking with figures is not often thought of as a creative process, yet it seems to share many of the characteristics associated with creativity. A recent book on creativity contains the following thoughts on the matter:

> The ability to see patterns in data and the ability to sense problems are characteristics usually included in creativity. The capacity to be puzzled, a characteristic which has motivational features too, may be very important. A keen observer once said that part of Einstein's genius was his inability to understand the obvious. Thus the rejection of one's own and other people's superficial explanations and the ability to know when you don't know may be crucial to making original contributions.
>
> The ability to sense ambiguities and to question effectively—an ability which might be described as "curiosity in action"—may be important in creative activity.[1]

Is it not striking how much of the above description applies directly to the subject of this book?

In this chapter we will investigate some creative techniques for increasing insight, i.e. *noticing absences, checking for consistency,* and *broadening understanding*. The first two of these topics deal with some creative techniques of looking that naturally have results on thinking. The last topic is more on thinking with an inevitable impact on ways of looking.

Noticing Absences

"There is not one among them
but I dote on his very absence"

Shakespeare

The fact that something is missing, is often a valuable piece of information. (In certain circles, there is often more discussion about who was *not* rather than who was invited to a high society party.) Nevertheless, psychological research by Jerome

Bruner and others suggests that, in general, we avoid using negative instances (the *absence* of something) as a way to gain information. Perhaps it is just harder to notice something is missing; for if it is not there, how can you tell that it is not present. Remember hearing about the schoolteacher who asked the pupils in her class who were *absent* to raise their hands so she would know who was missing. Similarly it is difficult for the missing things in a report to signal their absence.

Nonetheless, it is possible to go looking for those missing things, even though it may take some conscious effort. Of course, ultimately the way the teacher finds out who is absent is by consulting a list of all the pupils who are supposed to be in class. This notion of a *list* is really at the heart of detecting absences. Unfortunately, the lists available in business are not as nice and neat as the one used by the teacher.

Expectations can act as a kind of list; so can *norms*. The differences and comparisons of expectations and norms that were talked about in Chapter 5, in a sense, can be considered as *absences*. For instance, you know that an unusual number of new orders came in last month, but the gross sales figures do not seem to show the expected increase. Thus you may be on to something which would bear investigation.

Symmetry can be used to create expectations that form a spur-of-the-moment list. If wage rates have gone up in one department, you tend to look for a symmetrical or parallel increase in other departments. If the volume of production goes up, you might expect that all the variable expenses would show a corresponding increase. Of course, not all parts of a business behave symmetrically, that is to say, not all parts of a business are analogous. There are gradings of difference between departments, products, individuals, etc. It is, however, an important part of the management job to become aware of and to monitor these differences. Searching for lack of symmetry is an excellent way to spotlight some of these discrepancies.

A more striking lack of symmetry is the *complete absence* of desired or expected data (as opposed to a *difference* in the

Exhibit 9-1

APPROXIMATION OF GIZMO LABOR COST FOR STAMPING

a) Data given
   total labor cost for month=$100,000,
   total number of workers=200,
   pieces stamped out=7,500,
   stamping workers=10.

b) Approximate average wage (total labor cost/total workers)= $100,000/200=$500.

c) Wages allocable to the stamping department = the average wage times the number of stamping workers = $500 × 10 = $5000.

d) Approximate cost of stamping labor per piece (stamping wages/ pieces) = $5000/7500 = $0.66.

---

data). How many times have you looked at some numbers and thought to yourself, "Why the devil doesn't it show how many —— there are?" Such a question could be dropped. Instead, you should probe to find out why such data are not shown. You should ask yourself what you would do with the data if you had them and whether there is any way of estimating the figure desired from the data on hand?

For instance, say that you were interested in knowing what the labor cost per Gizmo would be for stamping as opposed to polishing, assembling, etc. All you have are figures showing the total labor cost, the number of workers per operation, and the number of pieces worked on by each department. Exhibit 9-1 shows how you might go about approximating this labor cost.

You may realize that the accuracy of this approximation depends on whether the average wage in stamping differs greatly from that in other departments and it also depends on the assumption that the workers in stamping devote full time to that job. The raising of this kind of question is in itself a worthwhile result of attempting to approximate missing data. The process of calculation leads you further into a basic understanding of the figures. Making an approximation of missing data will often show you whether or not it would be really important to request or seek them out. You will get a feeling for the implications of what you could do with the data if you had them in more accurate form.

Symmetry can also be helpful in pointing up what data are missing. For example, let us say that the Gizmo stamping operation breaks down its report on the number of pieces into successful and rejected stampings. But the report from the assembly department simply lists a total without any such breakdown. You might ask yourself why the assembly department does not report rejected and successful assemblies. As a matter of fact, what is a reject in assembly? Does this kind of thing occur at all?

Again, these questions, arising from the figures that come across your desk, are important ways to learn about your business. Different people report differently, as do different departments, and different functional areas. Hence you could ask yourself: What is missing from the reports issued by a department, or an individual when compared to reports issued by other groups or individuals? What does the difference indicate? Should the missing data be requested or approximated? Even within a single report you may find instances of missing data although this will occur less frequently, since most reports tend to be laid out symmetrically in rows and columns.

"The little figure that wasn't there" is hard to find. The teacher can compare what she sees in the class with her attendance list. Unfortunately, the businessman has no such clear list. His own brain, experience, and his use of symmetry or parallelism, however, can provide him with the kinds of lists that will help him search out missing elements. Certainly searching for absences requires much more creativity and imagination than simply looking uncritically at what is presented to you.

Checking for Consistency

"Consistency thou art a jewel."

(Anon)

Most minds are sorely troubled by inconsistency. All our training teaches us to try to resolve the world into consistent patterns. In a way, lack of consistency in a set of figures can be considered a type of *noticeable absence*. Symmetry is also related to consistency, since a lack of consistency is often manifested in a lack of symmetry. In fact consistency, which involves logic and thought as well as visual appearance, is really a more complex form of symmetry.

Inconsistencies do not jump out from numbers. They must be searched for and coaxed into appearance. Exhibit 9-2 shows examples of various types of inconsistencies, none of which are very obvious at first glance.

ARITHMETICAL INCONSISTENCY

One important category of inconsistencies manifests itself in what appear to be mistakes in calculation. For example, a scanning of Exhibit 9-2 shows pretty quickly that the "Inspected" column is supposed to be the total of the two columns which follow it. By spot checking (discussed in Chapter 6), you can scan all the products to verify that the "Inspected" column does equal the total of the following two columns. In the case of the Gizmos, you find (using approximate figures), that $2200 + 1100 = 3300$ *not* 3500. In fact, checking the addition of the last digits, you note that $2 + 4$ does not equal 8. An accurate check of the Gizmo figures shows that the "Inspected" column differs by some 212 from the total of the other two columns. A clerical error? Possibly, but there may be some other explanation of a more serious nature, i.e. something relating to the measuring processes, the meaning of the column headings, etc. In any case, further investigation is called for.

Exhibit 9-2

GADGET CO. SHIPPING, INSPECTION AND PRODUCTION DATA

	Shipped	Inspected (immediately prior to shipping)	Completely produced	Taken from inventory and finished to customer specifications
Widgets	8550	8560	4750	3810
Gadgets	783	740	725	15
Gizmos	3578	3578	2242	1124
Whatsis	1005	1010	237	773
Thingamabobs	6413	5320	5160	160
Knick Knacks	492	492	35	457

In another instance, a report showed that sales had increased while the average sales per salesman had decreased and the number of salesmen had dropped. From an arithmetical point of view, this just could not be; something was wrong.

Calculating the Same Figure in Two Ways. One important approach to uncovering inconsistency involves calculating the same figure in two different ways. For instance, the figure in the "Inspected" column of Exhibit 9-2 could be considered one calculation of the inspection figure. Totaling the last two columns could be considered as another way of deriving the same figure. Let us take another example. You might verify a backlog figure by checking the sales minus the production plus the change in inventory. Sometimes you may not be able to get an exact second calculation, but you may be able to approximate it. For instance, you may know that labor generally runs about 30% of the cost of goods sold. You can check the cost-of-labor figure by comparing it with the figure for the cost of goods times 0.30.

This brings up the point that *percentages can be considered as alternative ways of looking at figures*. Sometimes just converting figures into percentages puts a different light on them, permitting new insights as well as uncovering further inconsistencies.

Another simple technique for catching inconsistencies involves cross-footing totals. In other words, you total the columns to see whether they check with the totals of the rows. In Exhibit 9-2 the sum of the totals of the last two columns should equal the total of the "Inspected" column. If you had done this and compared the two figures, you would have immediately learned that there was an inconsistency of some sort. (Accountants frequently use this kind of check.) In many reports like the one in Exhibit 9-2 it is not appropriate to present the report with column totals; e.g. when different products are involved, the total production of units may not mean very much. The point is that you may want to calculate such totals in order to uncover possible inconsistencies.

PROPORTIONATE INCONSISTENCY

Businessmen often assume that, all other things being equal, a certain rule of proportion will prevail between the various inputs and outputs of a business. Under this assumption, 20% of the customers should account for 20% of the sales volume, and the product with largest sales volume should contribute the largest volume of profit. Research into social phenomena (of course, business is a social entity) seems to indicate quite conclusively that behavior often does not exhibit this kind of consistency.

It may well be that something like 20% of your customers account for 85% of your sales, 80% of your profits come from 15% of your sales volume, and so on. In other words, there is a clustering effect such that a small group of inputs accounts for a much larger proportion of outputs. This kind of disproportion can exist in almost all areas of a company: expressions of employee grievances typically center in just a few leading individuals, a few machines represent a great majority of the funds invested in production equipment, and so forth.

Let us go back to Exhibit 5-1, Gadget Corp. distribution information, and pick out a few samples of disproportions. Six states account for 64% of the distributors, as was shown in Exhibit 5-2. Pennsylvania which has the highest number of B-type outlets ranks fifth in the number of A-type outlets. Sales in Pennsylvania were almost twice as great as for New Jersey, yet the number of distributors in Pennsylvania is approximately one-half the number in New Jersey.

Becoming aware of these disproportions can give you valuable insight into the problems and opportunities that lie behind the figures.

LOGICAL-CONCEPTUAL INCONSISTENCY

Another type of inconsistency is logical-conceptual rather than purely computational. Look at the symmetry of the first two columns in Exhibit 9-2. At first glance you probably notice that the two columns do not always agree—there is probably no reason why they should. Upon further inspection, you should notice, however, that for Gadgets and Thingamabobs the quantity shipped was greater than the quantity inspected. This does not seem logically plausible. So you try to arrive at an explanation: perhaps there were a few left-over items shown as inspected but not as shipped on the last report. This might do for Gadgets, but the difference in the case of the Thingamabobs is substantial enough to cast some doubt on that explanation. To resolve this, you might take a look at prior months to see whether this particular inconsistency had appeared before.

In an actual case, this type of inconsistency did appear and when checked out produced some intriguing results. First of all, it turned out that the clerical method of recording inspected items was very poor and resulted in some instances of double counting and others of lack of counting. It was also discovered that much too large a stock of inspected but unshipped items did exist. Moreover, it developed that some items were not receiving an inspection immediately prior to being shipped (very important in this company because of the nature of the product). Some questions were incidentally raised about the packing procedures. All of this was uncovered as the result of pursuing a logical inconsistency which showed up in some numbers.

Other examples of logical inconsistencies might be total sales going down while the number of customers increased, or working-capital needs increasing more than profits.

Emerson once said, "A foolish consistency is the hobgoblin of little minds..." It must be admitted that truth and consistency are not one and the same. Furthermore, seeming inconsistencies often have perfectly logical explanations. Yet inconsistency is worth ferreting out, for a lack of consistency often signals the presence of a problem or a need for investigation.

Broadening Understanding

"With all thy getting, get understanding."

Old Testament, Prov.

In one sense this whole book is basically aimed at suggesting ways by which you can deepen your understanding of a set of numbers, that is, comprehend what the figures are all about. The odds are high that any set of numbers that crosses your desk will contain at least some columns or rows of figures which you do not really understand, i.e. you will not have a clear idea of exactly what the figures are supposed to mean. Mastering this seemingly simple-minded type of understanding is not quite as easy as it may appear. But such understanding is surely the basis for almost any further analysis or interpretation.

PROBLEMS OF UNDERSTANDING

Usually numbers standing by themselves do not have the power to express what it is that they are supposed to represent.

Most groups of figures always have some words along: a report title, or perhaps some row or column headings.* In this way the world of numbers makes contact with the world of *semantics,* giving rise to a condition which, while in general illuminating, has its darker side. Semantic problems can be complex and have been the subject of many books. (Since we will not go into any detailed discussion of semantics here, you may want to browse through some of the books on semantics listed in the Bibliography.)

It is curious to note that custom has come to decree that the number of words on a page of figures should be held to a minimum—use of an abbreviated, shorthand style is almost mandatory. However, these few words not only start our thinking processes but continue to direct them. How little attention is paid to these few but incredibly important words which must inevitably accompany numbers!

Clarity of Meaning. Perhaps the major semantic problem which can arise involves the meaning of the words describing the numbers. Advertising slogans often carry figures which appear to be clear, but which upon closer examination become quite fuzzy.

Widgets are 20% more effective.

What is meant by "more effective"? "More effective" *than* what? What does "20% more" really mean? Figures issued by a company for internal consumption are not necessarily exempt from the same kind of confusion.

Sometimes the meaning of a figure seems quite clear until you try to figure out precisely what is included or excluded. For example, take the expression "average hourly wage." It certainly seems clear enough, but does this figure include vacation time and sick pay? Does it include a way of accounting for fringe benefits like stock options, discounts on company merchandise, or bonuses? Is overtime and double time premium included in the hourly wage rate? Expressions like "fixed

---

* Do not forget occasional footnotes.

A product may have undergone modifications over a period of time.

costs," "absenteeism rate," "profit," or "purchase discounts" prove equally ambiguous and elusive.

The Same Words Apply to Different Things. Many companies have various job titles applied regardless of the person holding the job. Yet all these individuals are different and probably perform somewhat different functions. For instance, a secretary for one boss may have very different duties from a secretary in a different department. (Further elaboration here might prove risqué.)

Take the historical prices of a product. There should not be much confusion about that, yet no doubt, the product has undergone modifications from time to time. It might not be fair to compare the price at one time with the price at a later date, since such prices may actually refer to somewhat different products.

The other part of this problem is, of course, that the same words may mean different things to people of different backgrounds and experiences. Let us take an inventory figure, for example. The man in charge of inventory sees it in terms of reorder levels and quantities. The salesman may see it in terms of lead times on delivery dates. The financial man sees it in terms of tied up cash and storage rentals.

Meaning is Influenced by Presentation.   What a number seems to be is also strongly affected, apart from any wording involved, by the way it is *presented*. The statistics books mentioned in the Bibliography abound with examples illustrating how graphs and charts can be manipulated so as to give a different appearance to the figures. As Chapter 7 pointed out, numbers seem different when placed in different contexts. By putting a medium-size figure next to a larger one, the former can be made to appear smaller.

Sometimes, figures are presented in smaller type
and therefore appear less important.

Everybody knows that embarrassing financial figures can be buried by sticking them in footnotes way at the end of a report.

TECHNIQUES TO IMPROVE UNDERSTANDING

It should by now be apparent that some conscious effort is required to penetrate ambiguities of what figures claim to be and arrive at a real understanding of them. The following techniques can help you in your conscious efforts and are specifically directed at helping overcome one or more of the problems outlined in the previous section.

Try Making Up the Report Once Yourself.   If you think that you really understand all the numbers in a report, here is how to find out for sure. See whether you can make up a monthly report yourself instead of having it prepared for you by a subordinate. Some businessmen have been forced to do this because a subordinate was sick. Inevitably they found that there was a great deal they did not know about the reported figures, their sources, their biases, etc.

If you feel you cannot spare the time to go through such an exercise, just pick a few items and check them thoroughly as though you were preparing the figures yourself. You are almost sure to find something about the company and the figures that you did not know before.

Discuss Figures with Somebody. Another way of broadening and testing your understanding of a report is to discuss it with somebody. If the person has absolutely no acquaintance with the figures, try to explain what they really mean, e.g. just what is meant by rejects, backlog, or purchased items. If you discuss the numbers with someone who is familiar with them, ask him what he thinks the figures represent. There will almost certainly be some difference of opinion which can lead to a fruitful discussion.

Conversation is known to have idea-producing properties, but it is curious that while businessmen frequently discuss problems, business deals, and so on, they rarely discuss projected figures or reported numbers *per se*.

Look at the Figures Several Different Times. As we have pointed out several times in this book, numbers are just loaded with meanings. Part of understanding figures involves becoming acquainted with the multiple aspects of a given number or set of numbers.

It is generally difficult to consider a number (or anything else for that matter) from many points of view at the same time. The mind just does not function well that way. You must start by making an effort to see the figure (and relate it) in ways other than you habitually do. (Some of the techniques in Chapter 7 and other chapters can be of help in this.) The implication, in any case, is that you must probably look at a given set of figures several times.

Perhaps you start by taking a bird's-eye view in order to get the general picture. Then you may focus upon particular numbers in order to find out a specific thing. Sometimes the first look serves to gather up the obvious or the most pressing items. With these things no longer cluttering your mind, you can look again in order to pick up whatever other information the figures contain.

Rather than spending twenty minutes all at one time studying a set of numbers, why not look ten minutes one day and ten minutes the next? This will give your subconscious time to function. You will have different things on your mind at the two different times and therefore may get more out of the numbers. Some research on problem solving seems to indicate that putting down a problem and picking it up later can be an excellent way to gain new insights. Why not apply the same strategy to thinking with figures!

Montaigne, the French philosopher, claimed that "Men are most apt to believe what they least understand." His proposed antidote for this condition, inscribed for his library, read: "I do not understand—I pause—I examine."

CHAPTER 10

Number Traps

"Error is all around us and creeps in at
the least opportunity."

Charles Nicolle

We do not live in the "best of all possible worlds" and so opportunities for error abound in the world of numbers as well as elsewhere. Figures, although frequently the clearest description of a situation, are far from perfect and contain many traps for the unwary.

Previous chapters have hinted at various problems which can arise in the use of figures. For several reasons, however, little emphasis has been put on the pitfalls. It has been said: "The man who makes no mistakes does not usually make anything."[1] You cannot fall into a number trap unless you are in fact thinking with figures. This book has been primarily directed at stimulating your ability to think with figures; with the full realization, however, that the more you deal with figures, the more you increase the possibility of misusing them (hopefully in a less than proportionate ratio). Worrying too much about mistakes can be very inhibiting and is perhaps one reason why so many people are "number shy."

One reason for limiting the emphasis on pitfalls is that several books, listed in the Bibliography, do a nice job of covering this subject. Again, beware of letting such books dampen your ardor and inhibit your ability to use numbers. "It is one thing

There is always a chance for error in the measurement process.

to show a man he is in error, and another to put him in possession of truth."[2]

In the last chapter, we emphasized the importance of understanding what figures *claim to be;* in this chapter we shall consider the other side of the coin, what figures *really are.* These two sides of the coin can often be as different as heads and tails. We will first discuss some problems in measurement, or what numbers really are. Then we will take a look at various kinds of errors which arise because of differences between what numbers claim to be and what they really are.

Measurement — What the Numbers Really Are

As you will recall, an earlier part of this book made the point that numbers generally imply some kind of measurement. Finding out what a number truly represents basically involves a careful consideration of the measuring process which generated the number. There are a great many more chances for error and bias in the measuring process than you might expect.

Let us take a hypothetical figure that might have crossed your desk and examine in detail the process by which that figure was generated. The figure you have in front of you claims to be the number of nails produced by a given machine during a particular shift. Let us suppose that you have clarified just exactly what this figure is supposed to mean: You know what kinds of nails are included and for what period of time, how rejected nails are treated in this figure, and how idle machine time is handled.

The first question is: What process was used to measure the quantity of nails? (They could have been counted individually, although that would have been somewhat impractical.) Let us assume you find out that they were weighed against some standard weight, i.e. a weight which is supposed to represent 1000 nails. Now, there is a chance that the scale was not correctly adjusted, i.e. there was some error within the measuring device. Even if it were working perfectly, it might have been misused. For instance, the man weighing the nails might have had a "butcher's thumb" which he managed to weigh in along with the nails. As if that were not enough, the results of the measuring process must be recorded or reported, and there is always some chance for error in this phase. Perhaps the pointer fell somewhere between two marks on the scale, and it was necessary to estimate the exact weight. Then too, the pointer has some width to it and the reading might be interpreted differently depending on what section of the indicator was looked at. We will not even mention the possibility of clerical error in recording the measurement or perhaps multiplication error in converting the weight back into a number of nails.

In a broader sense, what we mean by the *measurement process* is the *source* of the information whether it be a machine or a man or some combination of the two. If the measuring process involves a man, the source of error (or bias) can be conscious or unconscious. The competence with which the whole process is carried out results in something called the *reliability* of the figure. Becoming fully acquainted with the source of numerical information is good preparation for sidestepping many traps.

Perhaps it is not irrelevant to mention that the language of some primitive tribes has a verb structure built upon the *source* of the statement made. There are no tenses referring to time, instead there is one verbal mode for news from a neighbor, another for news coming from a friend through another friend, still another mode for something originating with the speaker. Perhaps these primitives would not fare too badly in the informational tangle that is business numbers.

What Figures Are and What They Claim to Be

Let us return to the figure which claims to be the number of nails produced. Let us suppose that by some miracle there were no errors in the measurement process. The point we wish to emphasize is that the figure recorded was the *weight* of the nails not the *number*—the conversion of weight into number was simply an automatic calculation bearing no relation to the *actual* number of nails. Of course, in general the weight may not be a bad indicator of the quantity of nails, but the two items are *not* the same thing. If, for instance, the size of nail or the weight of the raw material were changed, the same weight of output might contain different quantities of nails.

There is nothing wrong with using an indirect form of measurement, particularly in business, where many interesting phenomena simply can not be measured directly. Still, it is important to distinguish between what was actually measured and what is really desired. Ignorance of these differences can cause crucial misunderstandings about the business situations represented by the figures.

IRRELEVANT FIGURES

There are several ways in which figures can misrepresent a situation, the most blatant being when the figures are really irrelevant to what they claim to be. This is not always so easy to detect, as the following little puzzle illustrates.

Suppose that you go to your bank and deposit $100 and then, over the next five days, make the following withdrawals:

Your Account		Bank Ledger	
First day draw out	$40	leaves	$60,
Second day draw out	35	leaves	25,
Third day draw out	15	leaves	10,
Fourth day draw out	4	leaves	6,
Fifth day draw out	6	leaves	0.
Total	$100	Total	$101

The obvious question is why the Bank Ledger total shows an extra dollar. (Perhaps this just confirms your basic feeling that bankers are generally up to no good.)

The resolution of this little problem lies in the irrelevancy of totaling the Bank Ledger column. Any column of figures can be totaled. What the total means, however, is another question. Now the sum of the monies withdrawn should add up to the amount deposited (as it does in the left hand column), but there is no reason why the amounts left by withdrawals should total up to anything related to the original deposit. You may see this more clearly by considering a somewhat different version of the problem. Suppose you deposit $100 and then withdraw $1 each day, leaving $99 the first day, $98 the second day, and so on. You would certainly not expect that adding $99 to $98, etc. would have any relevance to the initial amount you deposited.

REALLY RELEVANT FIGURES UNSTATED

Sometimes the figures stated are perfectly accurate and even appropriate, but something important is left unstated. One regional sales manager tried to get authority to replace one of his six salesmen who had quit the previous month. Headquarters ignored his continued urgent requests. Then he got inspired and sent in a request but this time said nothing more than that *he had lost over 15% of his sales force.* Headquarters immediately gave him permission to replace his losses. The percentage figure left out the relevant fact that only one salesman out of six was involved.

Sometimes the number cited is a relevant but not the most relevant figure. For example, a report might emphasize the fact that sales have gone up. This is presented as an indication that the company situation is improving. Perhaps, the more appropriate fact to have presented was that profits had dropped significantly. A purchasing agent might bask in the glory of having reduced the cost of purchases when in fact he was still paying more for raw materials than any of his firm's competitors. In one sense, these omissions might be considered a form of the *noticeable absences* discussed in the previous chapter.

CONCEALED RELEVANCE

Perfectly relevant figures are sometimes presented, but the important facts are concealed rather than exposed by the figures. One of the most common ways of concealing something is to add together several numbers. It becomes, then, very hard to clearly separate out one of the original figures.

Many a firm continues to market a product which loses money because figures were never presented in *unaggregate* form for that particular product. Remember that almost every number involves some degree of summarization. While the virtues of summarization were extolled in Chapter 4, they can become vices in the hands of someone unscrupulous or just careless.

Making Use of Numbers

Using a number properly implies knowing exactly what it is and exactly what it claims to be. This does not guarantee, however, that it will always be used correctly. There are other problems which arise from the natural limitations of numbers, your calculations with them, and your possible logical errors.

LIMITATIONS OF NUMBERS

Chapter 2 emphasized the incomplete nature of numbers. They can report or describe only *part* of a situation. However, most of the uses for numbers involve decisions or actions about a *whole* situation. As a result, various assumptions about figures are always possible.

Thus, numbers should be thought of not as completely determinate, but rather as suggesting a range of possibilities. This means that there is always an air of uncertainty around numbers, and that there may be several possible explanations for a figure. Numbers that pertain to the future are of course even more uncertain.

Another factor contributing to the uncertainty of numbers is their approximate nature. Chapter 4 urged increased use of approximation. Nonetheless, it is important for you to remember what you are dealing with. Be sure that you take the level of approximation into account in any conclusions.

Numbers also tend to present the interpreter with too much information. There is an old saw on Madison Avenue which goes: "50% of advertising is waste, but no one can figure beforehand which 50%." A lot of the information imparted by a given group of numbers may be superfluous. It is just very hard to know in advance which part will be useless. That is to say, numbers report a lot of information from which you must make pertinent selections. Furthermore, numbers cannot get across their message by repetition or emphasis. Everyone knows that a good speech or written report should begin by stating what is going to be covered, covering it, and then summarizing what has been covered. Few numbers are ever presented in this kind of format.

All these limitations on figures are waves in the same sea of trouble; *numbers even when they are very accurate, are not the same thing as the situations they portray.* Numbers, like any description, whether it be about politics, sex, or business, must be distinguished from the thing being described. To clarify this point, imagine trying to describe an avocado to someone. The best way would be to buy an avocado and show it to the person. In other words, the most complete and true description of an item is an example of the item itself. A description of something is by definition different from the thing itself. You cannot spend the number in your bankbook; you can only spend what it represents, money on deposit in your account at the bank.

Remember the alleged salad-oil swindles of a few years ago? They were possible only because many intelligent businessmen confused numbers with the reality they were supposed to represent. It must have been quite a shock to them when they discovered the difference between the number (reported amount of oil) and the reality (actual quantity of oil).

ERRORS IN CALCULATION

To effectively pull information out of a set of numbers, it is usually necessary to make some further calculations. (Many of the approaches suggested in this book involve some kind of calculation.) Numbers, however, are tricky, and great care must be taken even in simple arithmetical operations. It is hard enough to just add a column of figures without error, and it is all too easy to add percentages which do not apply to the same base or to add averages incorrectly, etc. Several examples of this were given in Chapter 4, and here are two more for your amusement:

1. Slide a card down the following column of figures, adding them one at a time as they are uncovered and saying the totals out loud.

10
10
1000
10
10
1000
1000
10
10
1000
10
10
1000
10
1000
10
───

Did you get a total of seven thousand? Most people do. It is not correct. The proper total is six thousand one hundred as you can easily verify by adding the column in the normal way.

2. Your firm sells Widgets at a price of 2 for $5. A rival sells them at a price of 3 for $5. You and your rival each sell 300 Widgets a month. Thus your monthly receipts are $750 while your rival takes in $500. Together you take in $1250.

Suppose that you and your competitor decide on a joint venture to sell Widgets at the rate of 5 for $10 (2 for $5 plus 3 for $5). Your rival keeps the books and reports that at the end of the first month, receipts for the 600 Widgets sold jointly are only $1200. Has your rival pocketed $50?

No, there is nothing wrong here. Things have worked out just as they should only not as you calculated. Do you see why the receipts should be less under the joint venture?

LOGICAL TRAPS

Feathers are light.

Light comes from the sun.

Therefore, feathers come from the sun.

This represents a logical error of a rather whimsical variety. Here is not the proper place to delve into all the possible syllogistic mishaps. It is worth pointing out, however, that even if you know exactly what a figure is and what it claims to be, and even if you do not make any calculational mistakes, your conclusions may still be erroneous, simply because your reasoning is faulty. For instance, you may make a generalization without enough instances to properly support it, or accept a generalization as though it were always true, or apply a theory to a situation where it is not appropriate.

Figure 10-1

There is one particular kind of interpretation which probably occupies a good deal of your attention. As a businessman, you are continually seeking *causes* for situations, causes which you try to deduce from the numbers. However, no seeming relationship between two numbers (or sets of numbers) can ever *prove* causality; it can only suggest a number of logical possibilities:

a) chance was really the cause,

b) *A* caused *B*,

c) *B* caused *A*,

d) both *A* and *B* were caused by a third factor, *C*.

There was a wonderful story reported quite some time ago which beautifully illustrates the problem inherent in causal inference. It seems that some museum officials noticed attendance figures rising quite sharply and made great plans for expansion. Suddenly, just as new construction was about to start, attendance inexplicably dropped to its former level and continued to remain low. The explanation was only uncovered after some diligent thought. The museum executives discovered that a little gray building had been constructed next to the museum. This unimposing building turned out to be a public rest room.[3]

Often the mere *presence* of numbers gives the impression of careful thought and measurement, but this, of course, is not always the case. Neither should you always believe that just because a figure is *precise,* it is correct. Another type of mental seduction can occur when you are confronted by inconclusive figures, especially if there are a great many of them. An assembly of large quantities of incorrect or indecisive data does not necessarily produce reliable conclusions. Beware of using

Figure 10-2

numbers as a drunk uses a lamp post, "more for support than for illumination."

Bias and the Basic Sources of Error

It may be well to restate and review briefly the four interrelated sources of problems and errors which have emerged from the previous discussion.

Misunderstanding of what a figure is really supposed to be or mean is an all-pervasive cause for error. *Unreliable figures* are also frequent causes of trouble. How good and accurate was the process of measurement? Was there much chance for error? Would you get the same figure if the measurement were made again? These are the kinds of questions which will determine the reliability of a given figure. *Misuse* of numbers can occur for many reasons, even if the numbers are perfectly reliable and well understood.

There is a fourth source of error which is intimately connected with all of the others: *bias*. Everybody has his individual point of view and that is his bias. We tend to notice numbers which bear out our position or bring pleasant tidings. We overlook data which contradict our feelings or bear bad news. You must constantly examine figures with an open mind. Darwin claimed that when he came across data unfavorable to his hypothesis, he made special note of it because he knew such data had a way of slipping his memory more readily than favorable facts. Even a machine can have a bias determined by its mechanical construction and the way it operates.

Any time you look at numbers, you must question how the information could have been known in the first place. For instance, a figure about the number of rats in New York city certainly raises a question about how the data were collected. Who (or what) presented the numbers to you? What is his (or its) position? What is his (or its) background? What interest does he (or it) have at stake? If you ask this type of question, you will become aware of the possible bias that might have affected the numbers and their presentation.

Remember that the generation of any figure usually involves multiple judgments, made by different people with differing types of, and approaches to, judging. Bias can quite often be unintentional or unconscious as well as planned.

Try this well-known psychological experiment in perception. (For our purposes we will call it *Instant Bias*.) It is a graphic demonstration of how easy it is to create bias and how hard it is to overcome.

Study the picture in Fig. 10-1 very carefully for a minute or so. Try to absorb as much detail as you can about the woman represented. Now take a look at Fig. 10-2 and decide whether you would characterize the woman in that picture as old or young, fairly attractive or reasonably ugly.

The odds are very high that you described the woman in Fig. 10-2 as old and reasonably ugly. Yet this same picture can also be perceived as that of a young, reasonably attractive woman. Look at the picture again. You are still likely to experience some difficulty in seeing the young, attractive woman. You have very quickly built up a strong bias which prevents you from seeing certain configurations of the picture. In fact, it may be difficult for you to break the bias without looking at the picture in Fig. 10-3 which gives you a clearer outline of the young-woman aspect of the ambiguous picture (Fig. 10-2). It helps to know that the younger woman is facing to your right and is looking away from you. Blocking off the picture (of the old woman) from the mouth down can also help you see the young woman. The chances are that you would have interpreted the ambiguous picture (Fig. 10-2) as the young woman if you had first been preconditioned by the picture in Fig. 10-3.

Figure 10-3

So when you look at numbers, you should realize that what you see and pick out is at least in part determined by what you know or expect, i.e. by your bias.

Techniques to Avoid Traps

Here are some specific approaches and states of mind which can help minimize the number of times you get trapped by numbers.

CHECK THE REASONABLENESS OF THE FIGURES

Do the numbers make sense? Check the figures against what you know or expect and verify any large discrepancies. This kind of checking typically involves several translations between the world of figures and the real business situations they represent. Do not be afraid of testing the figures against reality.

There is a story of a professor in the Middle Ages who was dismissed from the faculty of a university. During a long and bitter debate about the number of teeth in a horse's mouth, he had the audacity to bring in a horse!

GET SPECIFIC

Think of all the questions it was necessary to ask to pin down just what a number is and what it claims to be. It is not always easy to get answers to such questions. A favorite (and irrelevant) answer nowadays is that, "The computer figured it out— what more do you want to know!" You must pin down things the way a lawyer pins down a witness in a cross examination.

PRESUME ERROR

Take a sort of "devil's advocate" frame of mind. Work on the assumption that any group of figures presented to you contains an error. You may want to spot check some of the column totals as suggested in Chapter 6 or look for inconsistencies in some of the ways suggested in Chapter 9.

Unfortunately as a businessman you must, of necessity, continually check for errors. Clerical errors, for example, are inevitable, and it is part of your responsibility to control them. If you never literally *search* for errors, you will find that people preparing reports for you become less careful, and that the actual number of errors will increase.

BE TENTATIVE, IF POSSIBLE

Remember that numbers in and of themselves rarely prove anything. Numbers just provide material for thought. Observing something is very different from proving it. Speculation is different from thorough inquiry.

Actually, you are better off making too many inferences than not enough. In any situation there are always multiple factors at work. Conditions are not usually controlled, thus the reported (or projected) figures reflect the complexity of many interacting factors. Do not fall victim to the fallacy of a single cause. "If, when the tide is falling, you take out water with a twopenny pail, you and the moon can do a great deal."

Being tentative is not easy. John Dewey pointed out that there is a problem in sustaining doubt because it creates mental discomfort and often gives rise to feelings of inferiority. Not all business situations permit you the privilege of reserving judgment. Usually, however, it is possible to be more tentative than you realize. Think of it as a luxury and revel in it!

IDENTIFY ASSUMPTIONS

Assumptions are necessary even though they cannot always be fully validated. But you should consciously try to *identify* both the assumptions in the figures themselves and in your methods of dealing with them. (Even questions are often based on assumptions.) To give yourself a little practice in this, try the posers in Exhibit 10-1. None of them require any complicated knowledge or calculation. They are not difficult, provided you do not make assumptions which will prevent you from seeing the solution.

LOOK FOR WHAT IS MISSING

The importance of what is missing was highlighted both in this chapter and the last. Any way of presenting a number is partial and incomplete—there are always things missing. A percentage figure lacks the raw data behind it. An average lacks any indication of the deviation of the various components from the average, etc. If you are aware of what elements are missing, you will have some protection against error.

Exhibit 10-1

PROBLEMS IN ASSUMPTION

1. An executive's brother died, but the man who died had no brother. How could this be?
2. Without taking your pencil off the page, connect all nine dots with four straight lines.

· · ·

· · ·

· · ·

3. Assume that a train travels at constant speed with no time for stops. You know that at exactly 4:00 the train will pass the Dalquid station. On the basis of this information, you guess at the train's speed and thereby estimate at what time it will pass the Muldruff station. Even though you *overestimate* the train's speed, it passes the Muldruff station *earlier* than you estimated. Otherwise your information was all correct and everything occurred just as you expected. How could this be?

Answers

1. The tendency is to assume that the executive is a man. Once you see that the executive could be a woman, the problem is easy. The executive is the sister of the man who died.

2. If you had trouble with this one, you probably made the assumption that the four straight lines would have to lie *within* the figure outlined by the nine dots:

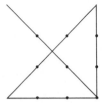

3. Chances are that you assumed the train would pass Dalquid *before* Muldruff like this:

— — — — → Dalquid   — — — — → Muldruff.
Train   (4:00)

But the situation is easily explained if you assume the train passes Muldruff *first:*

— — — — → Muldruff   — — — — → Dalquid.
Train   (4:00)

This chapter implies that dealing with figures is a tricky and time-consuming process. Unfortunately it is! But deal with numbers you must and avoid their pitfalls if you can. Becoming overly conscious of number traps can stifle you, yet a certain critical attitude can be very healthy. There is a difference between criticism and total scepticism. Francis Bacon once said, "Read not to contradict and confute, nor to believe and take for granted . . . but to weigh and consider."

Numbers do possess a certain magic, but sometimes it is black magic. Like the illusionist, numbers can make things appear to be other than they are. To quote an old saying meant for a slightly different context, "Safety in numbers is the maxim of the foolish."[4]

CHAPTER 11

Conclusion—Thinkers With Figures

"The thinker is pre-eminently a man who sees where others do not."

Ernest Dimnet

In *Through the Looking-Glass*, Alice reads the nonsense poem "Jabberwocky" and then exclaims, "Somehow it seems to fill my head with ideas—only I don't exactly know what they are!" To ensure that you are not left feeling this way, this concluding chapter pulls together the various strands of ideas and information which have been running through the previous chapters.

A Mind Deals With Figures

Most of this book has been concerned with the process by which a mind deals with figures. This process can be thought of in terms of three primary elements: the workings of the mind, the nature of numbers, and techniques to help the mind deal with the numbers.

WORKINGS OF THE MIND

The mind has extraordinary powers, many of which are only dimly understood. We often assume that the mind will function efficiently under any and all conditions. The fact is that it has many limitations and eccentricities. To improve your thinking with figures, you must come to know something of the way the mind operates. The user of figures should know his mind as well as an athlete knows his body or a musician his instrument. Exhibit 11-1 summarizes all the characteristics of the mind mentioned in the preceding chapters.

THE NATURE OF NUMBERS

If using the mind is analogous to playing a musical instrument, then figures would be comparable to musical notes. Just as a musician must know something about notes as well as his instrument; so the thinker-with-figures should know something about numbers. The nature of numbers is not at all obvious

Exhibit 11-1

1. The mind can be thought of in terms of a *storage* and a *processing* unit.

2. The processing unit has severe limitations:
   a) It has trouble with numbers of more than two or three digits.
   b) It can deal with only a few items at a time (apparently no more than six or seven at the most).
   c) It cannot absorb data too quickly.
   d) It falters when a chain of reasoning becomes too long.

3. The storage capacity (memory) of the mind is huge, but access is not easy and the region of search is quite limited. Memory seems to operate in terms of linked relationships or chains; i.e. thoughts about one thing lead to thoughts of other things.

4. The mind (and therefore perception) functions primarily in terms of *classifications* and *structures*.

5. The mind tends to develop habitual channels and patterns of approach around, in particular:
   a) what is familiar,
   b) what is easy,
   c) what is pleasant,
   d) what is close together.

6. The mind finds it easier to operate
   a) in terms of images,
   b) in terms of specifics,
   c) in terms of something known explicitly.

7. The mind is uncomfortable in the presence of
   a) uncertainty or doubt,
   b) lack of pattern or order.

8. Intuition or hunch is necessary but not always correct.

Exhibit 11-2

CHARACTERISTICS OF NUMBERS

Numbers are:

1. *artificial*—simply a useful invention,
2. *abstract*—can be applied to many entities,
3. *representational*—have meaning only in this way,
4. *condensed*—a compact way to present information,
5. *approximate*—always to some degree,
6. *indeterminate*—within certain limits, yet
7. *specific*—more precise than many other forms of communication,
8. *passive*—must be activated,
9. *summarizations*—always to some degree,
10. *partial*—can never portray the whole situation,
11. *common denominators*—greatly aid in making comparisons.

and, as a consequence, has been the subject of much philosophical debate over the ages. Some of the important characteristics of numbers are shown in Exhibit 11-2.

TECHNIQUES TO HELP THE MIND DEAL WITH FIGURES

To make music, a musician needs more than an understanding of notes and an instrument. He must also practice and develop a technique. In like fashion, the thinker with figures must develop his technique. Exhibit 11-3 lists most of the techniques mentioned in this book, arranged under various headings which suggest their different roles. Of course, all the categories overlap and are interrelated.

It should be apparent that almost all of these techniques were designed to overcome specific problems posed by either the characteristics of the mind or the nature of numbers. (In fact, most of the chapters in this book were organized around one or more of these specific problems.) Where the mind has limitations, something must be done to accommodate the numbers to those limitations. If the mind becomes inefficient in certain directions, ways must be found to channel it into more efficient directions.

Almost all the techniques in Exhibit 11-3 seek to accomplish one or more of the following interrelated things:

a) providing something specific to be done,
b) demanding conscious effort,
c) breaking habits,
d) suggesting new classifications,
e) developing structure.

These items are at the heart of improving your ability to think with figures. You should not feel that the approaches presented in this book are by any means complete. They should form the basis for the development of your own techniques and ideas, appropriate to your own needs and abilities.

Providing Something to be Done. Ask a friend to say anything he likes into the microphone of a home tape recorder. The chances are he will stammer and mumble something about not knowing what to say. *Anything* is all to often *nothing*. Once you have something specific to do, you can concentrate on it and attempt to do it. This is why most books on problem-solving emphasize the importance of *defining* the problem. You cannot solve a problem until you have identified it.

In this sense, all the techniques of Exhibit 11-3 represent *something* that you can do when confronted by numbers. These techniques provide you with points of view. You must have some point of view when you look at numbers because figures only provide material for thought. These points of view may be business oriented, or number oriented, or some combination of the two. Most of this text has been devoted to points of view that are more numerical in nature.

These numerical techniques give you a way to start, that is, a way to stimulate the storehouse of facts and ideas in your mind. A proverbial Greek phrase says, "The beginning is half the thing." Once you have that beginning our popular wisdom points out that, "One thing leads to another."

Exhibit 11-3

SUMMARY OF SUGGESTED TECHNIQUES

Preparation (thinking before you look)

Techniques	*Special Methods or Considerations*
Pinning down what is being looked for and why	Raising questions or hypotheses
Identifying assumptions	Considering restraints, excess resources, and "measures of goodness"
Clarifying expectations—they form a key basis for comparison	Constructing informal models

Simplification (making figures easier and more productive to look at)

Approximating	Using rounding
Summarizing	Using totals, subtotals, and averages
Sampling—systematic concentration on only part of the data	Using informal random, cluster, and stratified samples
Reducing redundancy—another way to reduce the quantity of data	

Things to Look For (comparison is the key)

Techniques	Special Methods or Considerations
Large items—both in an absolute and a relative sense	Using ratios and percentages
Differences { over time: between products, plants, individuals, averages: between what numbers are and what they are supposed to be, etc.	
Similarities	
Missing items—data lacking or results not present	Scanning by rows and columns; using expectations and symmetry
Inconsistency—arithmetical, proportionate, and logical-conceptual	Calculating the same figure in two different ways

Changing the Numbers (to generate new insights)

Rearranging—shifting the layout of the data	Using new cross classifications or a matrix form of layout
Changing units of measurement—restating numbers	Using larger, smaller, or different units
Changing number values—to see the effect on other numbers (the what-if approach)	Increasing or decreasing numbers; reallocating resources or relaxing constraints
Translating numbers—changing languages	Using graphs, formulas, or words
Transferring—applying numerical concepts used in one way to a new and different area	

Exhibit 11-3 (cont.)

Other Strategies (to increase understanding)

Techniques	Special Methods or Considerations
Finding out exactly what the figures are supposed to represent	Visualizing
Finding out what numbers really are	Finding the source and method of measurement; considering reliability and bias
Looking at the figures from several viewpoints	Looking at the same figures at different times; discussing the figures with someone else
Trying to put the report together yourself	
Looking at the usually slighted sections of the data	Focusing on unfamiliar, hard, or unpleasant areas

Attitudes

Presuming error—assuming the data contain mistakes of all kinds	Spot checking calculations
Getting specific	
Being tentative—remembering the uncertainty which always surrounds the implications of numbers	Developing multiple inferences

Demanding Conscious Effort. Using the techniques of this book will require a good deal of conscious effort. This is excellent and provides some of the benefits to be derived from the use of the many procedures described in this text. There is often a need to structure the efforts of the mind, since when left to itself it tends to muddle a great deal.

The use of pencil and paper is required in many of the approaches outlined in Exhibit 11-3. The dramatic result of using pencil and paper derives from the fact that these tools focus your attention and demand your conscious effort. "There is in the very gesture [of taking pen in hand] something imperative which the most wandering mind seldom resists."[1] Of course, using pencil and paper does have its frightening aspect. It often forces you to think things through much *too clearly!*

Calculation—in your head, with a slide rule, or on paper—is another type of conscious effort called for by the techniques in this book. Performing meaningful calculations with figures is one of the best possible ways to break down their passivity. Once you start to manipulate numbers, they cease to be meaningless globs and begin to take on a character of their own. You will find that even after idly calculating with a set of figures, you will have absorbed a great deal of information about their relationships, their relative sizes, etc. Calculation with figures makes them come alive.

Breaking Habits. Habits can be useful and necessary. Without them we would be like babes facing the complexities of everyday life, having to think out each action before taking it. However, this beneficial tendency of habit to make things automatic can also be harmful. A habit may have been quite functional as it was developing, but it now continues to operate in situations where it may no longer be appropriate. In a particular context, once we have started, habit may encourage us to continue down the same path, even though we keep meeting up with the same barriers. It is a little like the case of the drunken driver who rammed his car into a tree on the side of the road, backed up a little, and then went forward right into the same tree. He continued this strange exercise until a patrol car pulled up and the policeman demanded an explanation. The drunk exclaimed, "I'm sso glad you came offisher. I sheem to be losht in an impeneretable foresht."

When you back off and force yourself to try a new approach, you open up new perspectives by making yourself think less automatically and more consciously about the figures at hand. This does not mean that you should continually jump around. *Effective thinking with figures seems to consist in a kind of alternation between persistence and variety,* i.e. spending some time going down one track and then stopping and purposely changing tracks. Some of the techniques in Exhibit 11-3 will help you to penetrate deeply in a particular direction. Other techniques will encourage you to change viewpoints.

Suggesting Classifications. Most psychologists and semanticists seem to agree that a fundamental element of all perception or knowing is the act of categorization or classification. We classify items by means of what are technically called "sorting factors." Many of the techniques discussed in this book employ one or another sorting factor as an aid to insight. There is no question that what we perceive and how we act upon it depend to a large extent upon our classification of things.

Developing Structure. A well-known Zen *koan* (riddle or exercise) asks the student to imagine the sound of one hand clapping. Without delving into Buddhist philosophy, we can see that part of the puzzlement in this *koan* occurs because we are asked to imagine a two-object relationship (the clapping of one hand against another) in terms of only one object (one hand). In our world, *meaning always seems to involve relations between two or more items.* It is these various relationships which we call structure. Numbers after all deal not only with magnitude but order and relation as well. Thus, many of the approaches in this book suggest how to discover connections, relationships, or structures in the numbers with which you are called upon to deal.

THE IMPLICATIONS FOR REPORT MAKING

Our point of view has been primarily that of a businessman thinking with and deliberating upon figures that are presented to him. At one time or another, most businessmen also become involved in generating data or putting figures together for the use of someone else. The arrangement of the figures and their presentation greatly affect their meaning and context. The whole field of data display is an intriguing one in which there is much research being done and much work left to be done. Number reports do not exist by themselves. They are always one link in the chain of communication and information processing.

It should be apparent that the techniques of this book would have some application to the creation of reports. The reports could be made easier to deal with and the important items highlighted, etc. But remember that no matter how well a report is presented, there will always be some need for the recipient of the data to think with the figures.

The Nature of the Numbers Expert

It is the author's belief that the "numbers expert" uses a set of techniques somewhat like those described in this book. The numbers expert deals with business figures through numerical as well as business approaches. Most of what he does is so intuitive that he cannot fully describe the procedures or techniques he is using.

In the earlier stages of your development, you may have to devote more conscious intellectual effort to thinking with figures. You may want to periodically use this book as a reference to remind you of various possible avenues of exploration. You may feel a bit uncomfortable when you refer to this book or consciously carry out some of the ideas. The situation is not unlike that involved in learning a foreign language. There is a certain stage where you follow prescribed procedures rather arbitrarily. You feel awkward and not in complete control of what you are doing. Perhaps a certain amount of sheer imitation is involved. As you learn to deal with figures, it is entirely proper that you go through a superconscious phase prior to arriving at a more intuitive stage.

"Genius is knowing how to tackle a subject."[2] So, this book has set up some specific and formalized ways in which to "tackle" numbers. You must explore these ways on your own to find the ones that make sense for you. Then you must use them over and over until they become part of your own approach. The separate techniques described are not the art of thinking with figures. They must be welded together by each individual to form a meaningful style.

THE NUMBERS EXPERT AS A PROBLEM SOLVER

The "numbers" man is often thought of as a sort of Sherlock Holmes of the number world, as a deductive-analytical wizard. In a broader context, detectives as well as number experts are not only reasoners but also problem solvers. Some psychologists have defined problem solving as that frame of mind in which there is an awareness of a need to know something that is not presently known (at least not consciously). This definition certainly fits the businessman dealing with figures. Chapter 7 mentioned that in problem solving, it is important to have a "search model" or some kind of "anticipatory scheme." Most of the thoughts in this book are designed to help you develop your own "search model" for use in dealing with problems of numbers.

CONFIDENCE AND THE NUMBERS EXPERT

A highly successful basketball coach did not urge on his team with talk about "fight" and "spirit" but instead stressed the importance of "confidence" and "poise." Most experts in any field demonstrate a certain calm confidence which seems to banish fear, that great inhibitor which can prevent you from using the capabilities you do have. The psychologist Maslow points out that problem solvers have a special kinship with the unknown. They are

> uniformly unthreatened and unfrightened by the unknown. . . . They accept it, are comfortable with it and often are even more attracted by the unknown. They not only tolerate the ambiguous and unstructured, they like it.

Of course, it is difficult to have confidence without a certain competence. Hopefully this book can help you develop your confidence by showing you how to better utilize the number and business sense you already have. At the very least, you should now have no trouble spending time looking at figures; you know a number of things you can do that are likely to lead to insight. There are many people who spend only a few minutes looking at a sheet of figures because they literally would not know what to do if they spent any more time on it.

THERE'S MORE THAN LOGIC

Thinking with figures involves much more than just the application of rigorous logic. You must be willing to *play* with numbers. You must be willing to make bad hypotheses and errors. You must be willing to chase down a few alleys that turn out to be dead ends. There will always be an amount of seemingly wasted thought and effort. But this play is a necessary part of getting acquainted with the numbers and developing a foundation that will ultimately produce dramatic insight.

The muse of *creativity* must always hover near the numbers expert. Hunches, intuition, and guesswork are all part of the game. Newton claimed that, "No great discovery is made without a guess." Another mathematician added that reason is "an experiment carried out in the imagination. . . . When we find ourselves unable to reason...it is because our imagination is not touched."[3] Creativity with figures as well as elsewhere simply involves seeing things that others do not see.

Above all, the numbers expert must have a sense of *adventure:* a sense of *curiosity* and a desire to *explore.* You can never tell what you will find when you dig into figures. You must be impatient and want to know what lies hidden within the numbers that confront you. You must continually ask questions of the figures and the business situation they represent: Why are the numbers the way they are? What if they were different? You must be willing to try new techniques, new ideas. As an ancient philosopher exclaimed, "You will never find the unexpected unless you look for it!"

And so this book has tried to bring out the explorer in you by uncovering new paths along which you can pursue the important adventure of thinking with figures in business.

Notes

CHAPTER 1

1 Attributed to F. W. Parker.

CHAPTER 3

1 Written by Sir Arthur Eddington.
2 A point frequently made by Jerome Bruner in *A Study of Thinking* and elsewhere.
3 Discussed by Rudolph Flesch in *The Art of Clear Thinking* (see Bibliography).
4 John Lighton Synge, *Science: Sense and Nonsense* (see Bibliography).

CHAPTER 4

1 Attributed to C. Stanley Ogilvy.
2 Morris James Slonim, *Sampling in a Nutshell,* Simon and Schuster, New York, 1960. Quoted by permission of the publisher.

CHAPTER 5

1 For a more detailed presentation of this subject see Robert N. Anthony, "The Trouble with Profit Maximization," *Harvard Business Review,* November–December 1960.

CHAPTER 7

1 Discussed by A. V. Gordon Childe in *Man Makes Himself.*
2 Norton Juster, *The Phantom Tollbooth* (see Bibliography). Quoted by permission of the distributor, Random House.

CHAPTER 8

1 In particular, see the article, listed in the Bibliography, by P. R. Christensen entitled, "The Role of Intellectual Factors in Problem Solving."

CHAPTER 9

1 Calvin W. Taylor, *Creativity: Progress and Potential* (see Bibliography). Quoted by permission of the publisher.

CHAPTER 10

1 Attributed to a sermon of Bishop W. C. Magee.
2 John Locke.
3 *This Week Magazine,* April 17, 1948.
4 Attributed to C. C. Colton.

CHAPTER 11

1 Ernest Dimnet, *The Art of Thinking* (see Bibliography).
2 W. W. Sawyer, *Mathematician's Delight* (see Bibliography).
3 Ibid.

Bibliography

ON THINKING AND PROBLEM SOLVING

Beveridge, W. I. B. *The Art of Scientific Investigation*. Random House, New York.

Bross, I. D. *Design for Decision*. Macmillan, New York, 1953.

Bruner, J. S. *On Knowing: Essays for the Left Hand*. Harvard University Press, Cambridge 1963.

————, J. J. Goodnow, and G. A. Austin. *A Study of Thinking*. John Wiley, New York, 1956.

Christensen, P. R., J. W. Frick, J. P. Guilford, and P. R. Merrifield, "The Role of Intellectual Factors in Problem Solving," *Psychological Monographs General and Applied*, No. 529, 1962.

Dimnet, E. *The Art of Thinking*. Fawcett Publications, Greenwich, 1964.

Flesch, R. *The Art of Clear Thinking*. Collier Books, New York, 1962.

Hodnett, E. *The Art of Problem Solving*. Harper, New York, 1955.

Hyman, R., and B. Anderson. "Solving Problems," *International Science and Technology*, September, 1965.

Levenstein, A. *Use Your Head*. Macmillan, New York, 1965.

Newell, A., J. C. Shaw, and H. A. Simon. *Elements of a Theory of Human Problem Solving*. Rand Corporation, Santa Monica, 1957.

Osborn, A. F. *Applied Imagination*. Scribner's, New York, 1953.

Polya, G. *Mathematical Discovery: on Understanding, Learning and Teaching Problem Solving*. John Wiley, New York, 1962.

————. *How to Solve It*. Doubleday, New York, 1957.

ON STATISTICS AND PROBABILITY

Ekeblad, F. A. *The Statistical Method in Business*. John Wiley, New York, 1962.

Huff, D. *How to Lie with Statistics*. W. W. Norton, New York, 1954.

————. *How to Take a Chance*. W. W. Norton, New York, 1959.

Reichmann, W. J. *Use and Abuse of Statistics*. Oxford University Press, New York, 1962.

Slonim, M. J. *Sampling in a Nutshell.* Simon and Schuster, New York, 1960.

Stockton, J. R. *Business Statistics.* South Western Publishing Co., Cincinnati, 1958.

Tuttle, A. M. *Elementary Business and Economic Statistics.* McGraw Hill, New York, 1957.

Wallis, W. A. and H. V. Roberts. *Statistics, a New Approach.* Free Press, Glencoe, Ill., 1956.

ON "QUICK AND DIRTY" ARITHMETIC

Asimov, I. *Quick and Easy Math.* Houghton Mifflin, Boston, 1964.

Meyers, L. *High-Speed Math Self-Taught.* Pocket Books, New York, 1961.

Regnault, J. *Les Calculateurs Prodiges.* Payot, Paris, 1943.

Sticker, H. *How to Calculate Quickly.* Dover Publications, New York, 1955.

ON SEMANTICS

Hayakawa, S. I. *Language in Thought and Action,* 2nd ed. Harcourt Brace and World, New York, 1964.

Johnson, W. *Your Most Enchanted Listener.* Harper and Brothers, New York, 1956.

Upton, A. *Design for Thinking: a First Book in Semantics.* Stanford University Press, Stanford, California, 1961.

ON LINEAR PROGRAMMING

Ferguson, R. O., and L. F. Sargent. *Linear Programming: Fundamentals and Applications.* McGraw Hill, New York, 1958.

Heady, E. O., and W. Candler. *Linear Programming Methods.* Iowa State College Press, Ames, Iowa, 1958.

Loomba, N. P. *Linear Programming: An Introductory Analysis.* McGraw Hill, New York, 1964.

Meisels, K. *A Primer of Linear Programming.* New York University Press, New York, 1962.

MISCELLANEOUS SELECTIONS

Bell, C., C. Hammond, and R. B. Herrera. *Fundamentals of Arithmetic for Teachers.* John Wiley, New York, 1962.

Bowers, H. and Joan E. *Arithmetical Excursions.* Dover Publications, New York, 1961.

Carroll, L. *The Annotated Alice.* The World Publishing Co., New York, 1964.

Court, N. A. *Mathematics in Fun and in Earnest.* The New American Library, New York, 1961.

Juster, N. *The Phantom Tollbooth.* Epstein and Carroll, New York, 1962 (distributed by Random House).

Muckler F. A. and R. W. Obermayer. "Information Display," *International Science and Technology,* August, 1965.

Sawyer, W. W. *Mathematician's Delight.* Penguin Books, Baltimore, 1963.

Stokes, C. N. *Teaching the Meanings of Arithmetic.* Appleton-Century-Crofts, New York, 1951.

Synge, J. L. *Science: Sense and Nonsense.* J. Cape, London, 1951.

Taylor, C. W. *Creativity: Progress and Potential.* McGraw Hill, New York, 1964.

Zeisel, H. *Say It with Figures,* 4th ed. Harper, New York, 1957.

Index

Index